Grasp the Nettle

MAKING BIODYNAMIC FARMING & GARDENING WORK

PETER PROCTOR with GILLIAN COLE
ILLUSTRATED by TANA LYONS

RANDOM HOUSE
NEW ZEALAND

National Library of New Zealand Cataloguing-in-Publication Data

Proctor, Peter.
Grasp the nettle : making biodynamic farming and gardening work /
Peter Proctor with Gillian Cole ; Illustrations by Tana Lyons.
Previous ed.: 1997.
Includes bibliographical references and index.
ISBN 978 1 86941 657 7
1. Organic farming. 2. Organic gardening. I. Cole, Gillian, II. Lyons, Tana. III. Title.
631.584-dc 22

A RANDOM HOUSE BOOK
Published by
Random House New Zealand
18 Poland Road, Glenfield, Auckland, New Zealand
www.randomhouse.co.nz

First published 1997, reprinted 2000, 2002 (twice)
Revised edition 2004, reprinted 2007

ISBN 978 1 86941 657 7

Cover design: Katy Yiakmis
Cover photo: Peter Proctor
Printed in Australia by Griffin Press

Contents

Foreword

I feel special pleasure in writing a few lines to introduce this book and also to introduce the author. Peter Proctor leads an ordinary *grihastra* life surrounded by most of the worldly cares and responsibilities. He possesses a healthy body with an absolutely unassuming exterior. He has wedded spirituality to environmental and ecological farming.

His mission at this age of 68 years is to enlighten and train the farming communities, especially the youth of east and west alike. Peter has worked hard to promote biodynamic agriculture in Asian countries since 1993, and I feel he is having tremendous success in his endeavours.

I was given training in biodynamic agriculture by Peter in Hawke's Bay in New Zealand in 1993, and since then I have worked with him and his colleagues in New Zealand, Australia, Bangladesh and India, to popularise biodynamic farming. Now Peter has adopted India as his second home and spends two to three months a year there, from south to north, from the Arabian Sea coast to the great Himalayas.

His role as a teacher is important — it can never be overemphasised that it is the efficacy of the system and the calibre of the *guru* or teacher that count, and a mistake in the selection of these may render all effort in vain.

Grasp the Nettle is a treatise on the biodynamic agriculture system, and it deserves to be studied with close attention by those interested in spiritual, sustainable farming or *ahimsak kheti* (non-violent agriculture). One of the main objectives of biodynamics is to realise the truth depicted in the natural farming of the ancient sages and Veda, Upanishad and other scriptures of the Indian subcontinent.

To know the historical and philosophical background of a movement is to know something substantial about its validity and potential effectiveness as well as why it advocates what it does. Biodynamic agriculture or farming is an ecological, self-supporting farming system rather than an industrial or chemical approach to the production of food. It has no adverse environmental effects and it promotes soil enrichment, conservation and construction. Soil is viewed as a complex and living entity and is considered the prime capital and wealth of the farmer.

Dr Rudolf Steiner in 1924 described what is now known as biodynamic agriculture, a new way of thinking about the relationship of the earth and the soil to the forces of the cosmos. He pointed out how the health of the soil, plants, animals and human beings depends upon bringing nature into connection with the cosmic creative shaping forces.

This book, *Grasp the Nettle*, is an attempt to present this knowledge in a way that should help the practitioner make biodynamic farming and gardening work. The chapters on observation of plants and their forms can introduce the reader to many other ways of furthering his awareness of plant life on the farm.

Peter bases his knowledge on a lifetime of gardening and farming, and in particular working at the Hohepa Homes in Hawke's Bay. He has brought the biodynamic concepts to many, many people, in temperate and in tropical countries.

This volume should be kept in the libraries of all those who are interested in practising 'holistic farming'.

I wish every success and a healthy long life to the author to serve the world in the twenty-first century.

TGK Menon
Rural Agricultural Education Coordinator
Indore
January 1997

Preface to the original edition

I first made and used the biodynamic Preparation 500 on the Hohepa farm near Napier in 1966. Having being a student of Rudolf Steiner's work since the mid 1950s, I had learned about making 500 from Australian Robert Williams, who had been making it near Sydney since about 1938, and also from Alex Podolinsky. It is interesting to note that the first 500 in the southern hemisphere was made and applied by Bernard Crompton Smith in 1928 in Havelock North, New Zealand. Later the impulse was picked up by GB Winkfield, who made all the preparations after a trip to Switzerland, and subsequently shared his expertise with Robert Williams, who passed it back to farmers in New Zealand.

Many people were studying and working with biodynamics in the 1950s and later, and this has given a solid foundation to what is happening now, in the late 1990s. It was all pretty new to us in New Zealand at that stage. However, several people in Hawke's Bay at the time — John Donaldson, Gheit Wiersmar, Shirley Wall, Michael Jackson, and Shirley and Clifford Harmer — were noticing the change in soil structure and also the improvement in food quality after applying Preparation 500. In particular, John Donaldson was growing Sturmer apples and asparagus, and rearing poultry and pigs, and Gheit Wiersmar concentrated on carrots and potatoes. These products were my family's introduction to the wonderful taste of biodynamically grown food.

In 1973, when the late Tom Stevens, a dairy farmer from Kaukapakapa, was encouraged by his daughter Ina to come to Hohepa and tasted the Hohepa Golden Delicious apples, he wanted to use 500 on his cow paddocks. Why? 'Because,' he said, 'if you can grow apples as sweet as that, I could grow grass that's as sweet' — and he did!

Tom was, at that point, 72 years old. He had been dairy farming all his life and was considering retirement. But he equipped himself with a stirring machine and spray gear to apply the 500, and made a new start to his dairy farming. Tom was very impressed with the results he achieved, and loved showing people how his soil had improved.

Shortly after that, John Pearce and his wife Norrie, who as a child had been a neighbour of the Stevenses, paid them a visit while looking for ways to manage the farm they had recently bought. They quickly saw the advantages of biodynamic farming, which they applied to their 400-acre sheep and beef farm at Shelly Beach on the Kaipara Harbour in Northland.

One of the initial results from both these farms, which was a surprise to everyone, was that there were no cases of facial eczema in the sheep or cattle on either of their farms during a severe outbreak in Northland in the late 1970s. This outstanding result in animal health prompted a brief MAF investigation, but at that stage biodynamics was perhaps a little bit radical for many scientists and farmers!

The pioneering work of these and other families in the early days was invaluable — it helped bring biodynamic management into commercial enterprises.

Peter Proctor
Havelock North
January 1997

Preface to the revised edition

It is seven years since *Grasp the Nettle* was written, and now a few updates are necessary.

In this revised edition most of the text and content is the same, although there are one or two additions to provide clarification, and some new ideas on the way the preparations are applied. Two new appendices, 'Understanding the planting calendar' and 'Planets and the preparations' have been added. There is also an enlarged section on cowpat pit manure, which is proving to be a very useful medium to spread the effect of the preparations over the land.

Tana Lyons has redone some of her artwork, and I have tried to use new photographs where possible.

I have included an update on the biodynamic work in India, where much innovative practical work has been done which has had a beneficial flow-on effect to biodynamic practitioners in other countries. There is also a short update on the work of the Australian Biodynamic AgriCultural Association.

As I travel around to different countries I realise more and more how urgent is the need for the healing of our environment. Our air, our water and our soil have become so polluted. It is now becoming generally recognised in agricultural circles that the way the soils of our earth have been treated has been a huge contributing factor to this pollution. There is an urgent need for a change in direction towards the rebuilding of a living soil.

Biodynamic management systems as described in this book can be adapted to any soil to create this living soil in all countries in any part of our world. This means we do have directions in a practical way to heal the environment. Firstly we can eliminate all water-soluble agricultural chemicals, pesticides and weedicides from our farming systems. Then we can bring back biodiversity, and increase the soil humus levels which give soils the ability to hold moisture and thus indirectly improve our water supply and quality. Then there is the possibility of growing wholesome food, as described earlier, to support and nourish the body, the soul, and the spirit of all people. The right food will support the right thoughts.

When I see how the biodynamic management systems can dramatically improve any soils of any type and in any country in such a short time, I acknowledge with gratitude Rudolf Steiner's gift to the world. He made this knowledge available to all who care for and work on the land. I am sure the higher creative beings support in a spiritual way all those people on the land who have taken up this impulse. I wish these biodynamic farmers great and satisfying harvests.

Over recent months, from my experiences of many farms successfully striving for excellence in farming practice, has come the realisation that 'biodynamic agricultural farming methods make organic farming work'.

I would like to express my thanks to the many biodynamic farmers and other friends, and as well the publisher, who have helped me with words of encouragement to revise this book.

Peter Proctor
Hastings
March 2004

Introduction

if thou knowest it not,
this dying and becoming
thou art a troubled guest
across the world a'roaming ...
— Goethe

One of the underlying principles of biodynamic farming is the developing of lifegiving humus out of dead organic material. This biologically active humus is the basis of all living soil.

Can you recognise a healthy soil? Can you tell if your plants are healthy? Farmers, sometimes unwittingly, have taken on the responsibility to heal the earth and produce food that heals human beings. But a farmer who walks thoughtfully over the land and harvests crops with reverence produces a different product from one who drives a combine harvester all day with the radio playing.

Biodynamic agriculture is a method of farming that aims to treat the farm as a living system which interacts with the environment, to build healthy, living soil and to produce food that nourishes and vitalises and helps to develop mankind. The underlying principle of biodynamics is making life-giving compost out of dead material. The methods are derived from the teachings of Rudolf Steiner and subsequent practitioners.

Steiner built up his knowledge from keen observation of plant and animal forms and traditional peasant practice, scientific study and deep spiritual research. He gave his teaching on agriculture in the Agriculture Lectures in 1924, towards the end of his life.[1] By this time he had developed a high level of spiritual

---

1 The recent translation of Steiner's *Agriculture* by CE Creeger and M Gardner includes the first translation from the German of Steiner's lecture notes: Steiner (1933), *Agriculture* (Bio-Dynamic Association, Kimberton, PA).

awareness. His gift to the world is knowledge from the spiritual world that enables people to recreate and work with natural forces in the fields of education, medicine, religion, art and agriculture. Steiner taught that 'Matter is never without Spirit, and Spirit never without Matter.'

History of the movement

To understand biodynamic agriculture and its relevance for modern agriculture, it is a good idea to look at the background circumstances of Steiner's Agriculture Lectures, which he gave to a small group of farmers on a farm estate in Koberwitz, East Germany (now in the west of Poland, near the border with Austria).

In those days the conventional way of farming was what we would now call organic. Farmers did not use artificial fertilisers. They put all the dung from their overwintering barns back on the field, and along with growing soil-sustaining green crops and the sound use of crop rotation, they maintained a high soil fertility. However, even with good soil and animal husbandry, farmers found their crops were not doing as well as they should; seeds were not as viable, there was an increase in animal ill-health and food did not taste as good. Something needed to be done.

Farmers who knew of Rudolf Steiner's philosophy of spiritual science asked him if he could address these problems. Steiner pointed out that plants grew not only through the fertility of the soil, but also with support from the cosmos – the rhythms of the sun, moon, planets and the wider constellations of the zodiac. This cosmic support, he said, streams into the earth through the living nature of the soil and is important for the healthy growth and quality of the plants.

According to Steiner, as the earth becomes older the soil naturally becomes weaker and is less able to receive these cosmic rhythms than in previous times. He felt that a renewal in agriculture was necessary in order to find a way to re-enliven the earth so the cosmic energies could again stream strongly into the soil. He introduced the practice of making preparations based on cow manure, silica, and various herbal plants, to be used in order to open up the soil to these influences again. He also made plain the intimate connection between all living things and the cosmos, and the importance of learning the workings of the planets and the heavenly bodies.

Significance for the present

Modern agriculture has tried to come to terms with this ageing of the earth with a chemical approach. To maintain the levels of crop production needed, and to control the accompanying diseases, farmers use massive applications of a whole arsenal of sophisticated chemicals. But this, as we can already see, is leading to an environmental disaster with the poisoning of the soil, water and air.

At the same time, a huge amount of money is being spent on research into the use of chemicals and into genetically engineering plants and animals to solve problems that are in large part man-made. But some modern agricultural scientists appear to be unaware of the importance of the living quality of the soil for healthy growth.

Steiner advocated discontinuing the use of chemical fertilisers altogether. Because of their inherent lack of life, he felt, chemicals could not maintain life or increase fertility in the soil.

The answer to problems of human and animal health and degradation of our environment lies in maintaining a truly fertile soil, by practices such as crop rotations, incorporating plenty of organic matter and the biodynamic preparations as described in this book.

Farmers carry an enormous responsibility, not only in caring for the land but also in growing food which will be eaten by human beings, and which will give them life and vitality. The quality of the food we grow and eat is directly dependent on the cosmic energy that can come into a living soil, and this is what supports our daily life. According to Steiner, the life forces in our food influence the quality of our thinking and our interaction with other people.

Conscious thinking about and working with these cosmic formative forces, and applying this knowledge in making and using the biodynamic preparations, is what distinguishes biodynamic farming from organic farming and permaculture.

Biodynamic farmers and gardeners treat the farm as an individuality with regards to its ecological environment. They work to increase the cosmic formative forces that enhance plant and animal health and growth. It is important that they develop their powers of observation, since biodynamic management relies on working with the natural life processes in soil, plants and animals. Each farm or garden has its own unique microenvironment, and the farmer or gardener cannot rely on following a prescribed management plan such as the spray calendars used in conventional farming.

Grasp the Nettle encourages readers to observe and think about the forms and patterns in nature. For example, the spiral or vortex is fundamental to plant life. Biodynamic practice uses this same movement in stirring the biodynamic preparations. Biodynamic farmers can apply the knowledge gained from such observations to solving practical problems such as weed and pest management.

This book provides information on how to make and apply the biodynamic preparations; the times in the planetary calendar for carrying out various tasks; weed and pest management; and converting farms, orchards and gardens to biodynamic management.

The biodynamic preparations referred to in the book, which are essential ingredients of biodynamic farm management, can often be purchased from biodynamic associations (listed in Appendix 9). These associations can also provide advice about the Demeter standards required for certification as a biodynamic farm.

Biodynamic farmers try to work with the rhythms of the moon, planets and constellations. For an explanation of what is meant in the book by such terms as 'descending phase of the moon' and 'an air/light day', see Appendix 4, Understanding the planting calendar, and the New Zealand BioDynamic Association's *BioDynamic Farming and Gardening Planting Calendar* or Maria Thun's *Working on the Land and the Constellations* and *Gardening for Life the Biodynamic Way.*

The potential importance of biodynamic farming is being realised in countries such as India, where groups of dedicated practitioners are learning how to adapt the same principles to their particular conditions. This book includes observations based on experience in countries other than New Zealand, particularly India, Australia, the United States and in Europe.

Biodynamic farming is a new direction in agriculture that will benefit our planet in the future. I hope that this book will inspire all growers the world over to take up the challenge.

'A seminar at Kurinji'

Beneath the canopy of palm and neem
a new-made meeting hall was to be seen
Roof of coconut fragrant to most
with low rock walls and granite post

Mango and lime are at their peak
with wattle, mahogany, rosewood and teak.
All makes for pleasant cooling shade
to listen to farming plans well laid.
Rice-flour patterns at entrance welcome
A snake slithers to its home garden.

Eighty farmers and wives in white
waiting to hear the message right
Of cowhorns, compost and silica pure
and structure humus and cow manure.
Bananas, pineapples they grow,
cashews, coffee and some NGOs

Kurinji has with very much care
prepared a seminar that all can share
Liquid made and compost too
and horns are filled with dung so new
and also the BD orchard to view.

Many's the doubt that needs to be answered
of this direction to be mastered
But this courage now to change the way
and let 500 compost rule the day.

— Peter Proctor

The spiral and its expression in nature — water, weather and plant forms

1

Have you ever noticed that water from a hose pipe running down a paved path does not go in a straight line? It starts to move of itself — it meanders and spirals, and if you observe closely, you will see a pulsing movement. This pulsing is the beginning of the vortex.

The form of the vortex is manifested in many different ways in nature. Galaxies, for instance, move around in great spirals, and spiral movements are the basis of cyclones and anticyclones in weather systems. Observation of the connection of the vortex with life may help the understanding of biodynamic practices, such as the stirring of the preparations.

What happens in a vortex? There is a continuous, two-way rhythmical movement of water (or air), expanding and contracting. The water is moving at different speeds — slower at the edge and faster as it moves inwards and downwards and then up and out again. It is amazing that no particle of water is moving at the same speed as any other. In a large enough body of water the particles furthest from the vortex do not move at all and become still. In a running stream you can see all kinds of intricate swirling and vortices as the water moves in many different ways at once.

The intricacies of vortices in nature have been described by Theodor Schwenk in *Sensitive Chaos* (1965). According to Schwenk, vortices are created when two streams of water move past each other at different speeds. A hollow develops, into which oxygen flows: 'Boundary surfaces, with their rhythmical processes are the birthplaces of living things.'

The association of the vortex with pulsing, the life-bringing process, is the basis of many biodynamic practices. Vortices are formed during hand-stirring of the preparations, liquid manure and cowpat pit. The Virbela flowform has been specially developed to induce spiral vortices in the flowing water as a method of stirring preparations.

When we recreate this vortex in biodynamic farming, we are connecting with the universal creative water rhythms or pulse within the body of the earth. This can be found in all living things, for example in the heartbeat (see Chapter 4, 'Flowforms'). It is exciting to discover the expression of the vortex in spiral forms in nature.

Spirals in nature

In water spouts and clouds

Often on the coast in a windy bay, spiralling waterspouts can be seen moving dramatically across the sea. Tornadoes whirling across the land build up tremendous power. And if you stand on top of any part of the main New Zealand dividing range during a strong westerly airflow, you can observe the clouds spiralling high above as they blow in from the west.

The Meteorological Service of New Zealand has a speeded-up film made from satellite photos of weather patterns across the Tasman Sea. The film shows the high and low weather systems in inward- and outward-spiralling forms (cyclones and anticyclones), which look for all the world like a mighty river in turbulent flood.

In rivers

Any river, whether in flood or not, shows a pronounced turning, twisting, spiralling as it flows through gorge or over plain.

In shells

On the beach at the high-tide mark you can often pick up shells which show the varying, beautiful forms of the spiral — think, for example, of the nautilus or the turret shell. The large New Zealand bush snail also has a strikingly spiralled shell.

Turret shell

In leaves

One of the spirals best known to all New Zealanders is the majestic unfolding spiral of the ponga fern (*Dicksonia fibrosa*).

This spiralling can also often be seen clearly if you look down on a plant stem and observe how the leaf nodes gently spiral in two directions. This is particularly noticeable in one of the biodynamic preparation plants, the stinging nettle, *Urtica dioica*. The same effect is dramatically shown in the tight leaf configuration of many conifers such as the silver spruce (*Abies pinsapo*), or the Australian bunyan pine (*Araucaria bidwillii*).

Further obvious spirals in nature can be seen in the growth habits of climbing plants such as the clematis spp. and the New Zealand bush lawyer (*Rubus australis*). Kowhai leaves (*Sophora microphylla*) also unfold in a spiral motion.

Look at the spiral tendrils on pumpkin and cucumber plants and the spiral pattern in which Brussels sprouts are arranged around the stem of the plant.

Ponga fern

The spirally arranged frond scars on the stem of Phoenix palms (*Phoenix canariensis*) where the fronds have been discarded make it look for all the world like a great pineapple.

A spiral is made up of a series of halfmoon shapes — the form in which water expresses itself. This watery form can be seen mainly expressed in the leaves, but also in other parts of plants.

In flowers

Have you noticed the wonderful patterns in the flowers of the Compositae (daisy) family? In the centre of a composite flower such as a chrysanthemum, marguerite daisy, sunflower or single calendula, all the small unopened buds form a two-way spiral.

What more beautiful than the spiralling expressed in the opening of a rose bud? See how the petals exhibit this delicate beauty as the spiral unfolds around the base of the bud.

You can also observe spirals in many other flowers, such as the unopened buds of flax flowers, hollyhocks, convolvulus and campanulas. The heads of the Romanesque broccoli show double spiralling.

In fruits

Various fruits are in the form of a spiral. The pine cone, for instance, actually spirals two ways — a long spiral and a short spiral of different lengths, going around the cone in opposite directions. Fruits such as pineapples, strawberries and raspberries show similar two-way spirals.

Consider the marvels of the pea family (Leguminosae), and the way the pods display many spiral forms as they explode to disperse their seeds. Sweet peas, broom and gorse have these very twisted pods; and peas, beans and sweet peas show this spiralling in the twisting stems of their tendril-like leaves.

Kauri cone

With such a tapestry of spiralling forms in nature, can you appreciate the life-giving ability of the vortex? Try to imagine the formation of the plant as a dynamic flowing process of which the physical plant is the end result. What we see in the spiral plant form is the memory of the vortex 'frozen' into that form. Each plant expresses this water movement in a slightly different way.

A closer look at plant forms   **2**

Elements

Much of the basic form of plants, such as the shape of their leaves, fruits and flowers, can be attributed to the action of four elements that we continually experience around us and take for granted. Life on earth is supported by warmth, air/light, water, and solidity. Because our world has always been part of us, and is so harmonious and perfect, we do not stop to think about the environment that supports it.

It is interesting to consider the stages of growth of a plant in relation to the elements. They fall into a logical progression: the roots are the most solid part; the green leaves are the watery part; the colour of the flowers is connected to the light; and the fruits and seeds are ripened by the warmth.

Roots   —   Solidity

Leaves   —   Water

Flowers   —   Light

Fruits   —   Warmth

These four elements have been studied by Rudolf Steiner and later by Guenther Wachsmuth in *The Etheric Formative Forces* (1932). Both Steiner and Wachsmuth described the characteristic forms they felt were typical of the four elements. To the cosmic energy force that supports life, Steiner gave the name 'etheric'; the force that holds and gives shape to plants he called the 'etheric formative force'. If we look at the typical shapes expressed by the elements, it is possible to see in which element a plant is living, and how these forms intermingle.

Warmth

Warmth spreads out and diffuses everywhere. It has no form or solidity and we experience it only by feeling. It is either too much, too little or just right. Warmth is supportive.

Warmth is expressed by a sphere, typified in nature by the roundness of most fruits, for example pumpkin, apple, or bean seed. This warmth element has been named *warmth ether*.

Light

Light is also without form; it spreads over the earth and diffuses everywhere. But we can see light — for example, in a flash of lightning or in the billowing flames of a bonfire — and we can see the lack of it. Light is more dense than warmth. It is interesting to consider each of these two elements separately — warmth without light, and light without warmth.

Light and air show a triangulation, which can be seen in forked lightning, or in light rays when you squint at a candle flame. The airy light element has been named *light ether*.

Water

Water is more dense and able to hold a shape briefly. It can be touched, it can run through one's fingers. Water has the ability to be mobile and continually changing. It goes through a whole transition of density, from airy mist to drops of rain to flowing rivers to mighty moving seas, and at the poles, solid ice. Within all these states of water on earth there is an amazing variety of forms.

Water takes on a halfmoon form, indications of which are so often seen in its spiralling, meandering, wave-rolling forms. The name given to this element takes a little understanding. Because water supports organic chemical changes in the leaf of the plant, it has been given the name *chemical ether*. Another aspect of water is that it supports sound: when there is moisture in the air, sound from afar is carried and enhanced. This prompts the name of *tone* or *sound ether*.

Solidity

The element of *solidity* is the one with which we are most familiar. It holds its shape, is fixed, and is the densest state of the four elements.

Solidity is perhaps best represented by the cube, which typifies the final condensation and is the densest of the ethers. The cube is the crystalline form exhibited by common salt, which is present in the roots of many food plants. The name given to this element is *life ether*, meaning that it is present in the solidity of the earth which gives life support to all living creatures. A typical solidification of ether is seen in tree trunks. The wood from which your table is made contains material which once bore water and is now dense and solid, hardened by life forces.

These ether forces give rise to plant forms of infinite variety.

Plants and the elements

The form of a plant provides an expression of the influences developing it and also supporting it during its present growth. At each point of growth there is a different type of form.

Roots and stems: mineral/earth ether

Roots show a solid, earthy, mineral nature, which is associated with a high salt content. The cube form can be seen when the mineral nature extends up the stems, resulting in square stems such as in the Labiatae family (lavender and thyme). This square stem form is often found in plants with healing properties. Some plants, for example bananas and Red Delicious apples, even show an echo of this square form in their fruits.

Native mint

Leaves: water/chemical ether

Leaves are essentially the watery part of the plant. A predominance of the watery nature results in a typical leaf form — the halfmoon or spiral or river-meander or wavy form. Most New Zealand native plants, for example the taupata (*Coprosma repens*), show this watery form in their oval-shaped leaves.

Taupata

This water activity in the leaves and stems also brings about chemical changes. The main substance manufactured through photosynthesis is starch, such as in the potato. Starch can be transformed into a variety of other substances, such as cellulose, and various proteins that the plant needs. The process of photosynthesis through which plants build up carbohydrates and protein from carbon, hydrogen, oxygen, nitrogen and sulphur is a wonderful and essential creative chemical process.

Think of the chemical processes involved in producing the range of essential oils made by plants. For example, many different plants, originating all over the world, produce the lemon scent — lemon verbena, lemon balm, lemon geranium, lemongrass, New Zealand lemonwood (tarata) as well as the citrus. What is the common factor that enables these plants to make this scent?

Flowers: light/air ether

Compare the flowing, watery, oval leaf-form of most New Zealand native plants with the narrow, hard leaves of most Australian plants. The leaves of the eucalypts, acacias and callistemon (bottlebrush) have a sharper, lighter, triangular nature. This expanding, light, airy activity is particularly associated with flower forms. See how the acacia leaves in the drawing seem about to extend into colourful flowers?

Have you noticed the triangular form of petals in a daisy flower, or the five triangular petals of a single rose or petunia which form a pentagram. South African plants like the protea show a similar light

Acacia

Wheat

nature. In India, the harsh, brittle light has resulted in many leguminous plants with finely divided leaves like flower petals.

All the monocotyledon plants, including the grasses and grains, show a predominance of the light nature in their triangular forms. All the leaves of the grass family are in the form of an isosceles triangle. Wheat shows a combination of light, warmth and earthy nature in its round and triangular grains formed into the square-shaped ears.

You can expect that any plant showing the triangular form will respond well to application of the biodynamic Preparation 501 (see Chapter 5). The silica crystals from which this preparation is made also have a triangular form, which connects them to the same light nature.

Carrots have a triangular form in both the leaves and the roots and also respond well to 501. The light nature is so strongly connected to this plant that the colour, normally associated with flowers, extends right down into the darkness of the earth.

Fruit: warmth ether

Now look at the round, expansive form of pumpkins. This roundness and their colour can be related to warmth. Fruit and seeds generally can be related to a warmth process. Seeds need warmth to germinate and the plant needs warmth to develop its seeds. This round form also extends to leaves, for instance in the nasturtium, and tropical plants such as the fruit salad plant (*Monstera deliciosa*).

It can be an exciting experience when you start to notice the incredible variety of plant forms. Some show a mixture of forms; for example, the leek leaf shows a triangular, light-dominated leaf, while the seed head is a large sphere, typical of the warmth process. Each individual flower on this seed head is triangular, and so are the seeds.

The difference between the relative role of the various ethers in different countries can be seen in the flower, fruit and leaf forms. For instance, in New Zealand where the climate is mild and with a high, well-distributed rainfall, the watery influences can be seen in the leaf forms and minimal flowers and fruits; the leafiness is predominant. But in Australia, where

Leek seed head

there is much more light and warmth, the triangular form and to a certain degree the rounded forms of fruits are predominant.

For instance, observe the eucalypt flowers which show a triangular, light form. As they develop they receive more warmth and form rounded fruits. The eucalyptus gum nut is five-sided, with little triangles on top.

Most Australian tree fruits are hard and woody. By contrast, only one New Zealand conifer, the kauri (*Agathis australis*), forms a hard cone. The rest, the totara (*Podocarpus totara*), rimu (*Dacrydium cupressinum*) and matai (*Podocarpus spicatus*), develop seed on an open berry, reflecting the more watery New Zealand environment.

Development of eucalyptus from flower to gum nut

Plants, numbers and patterns[1]

If you compare the form of various plants you will see that they are generally regular, with different numbers of petals and leaflets. The lily family (Liliaceae) have a three and six formation, with three petals inside and three outside. Hyacinths, tulips and daffodils are similar.

The eucalypt family, too, shows a great regularity of numbers, particularly on the opening of the seed case. Different species can have three, four or five openings. The *Pinus* genus can have needles in bundles of two, three and five, depending on species: eg Scots pine *Pinus sylvatica* has two and *Pinus radiata* has bundles of five. Flowers in the Rosaceae family, which includes roses, plums, blackberries, strawberries and the New Zealand native tataramoa (bush lawyer), typically have five petals.

Other plants, such as cabbages and clematis, have four petals in a flower. Poppies have four petals but their fruit capsule is divided into sixteen. The passionfruit flower shows a seven and ten formation. Could these regular numbers have a relationship to the mathematical laws exhibited by our planetary or zodiac systems?

---

1 For further illustrations of plant forms see Grohmann, *The Plant* (1974).

If you cut an apple across the middle you can see a five-pointed star in the centre. Cut a thin slice and watch as it dries: you will see the outline of the blossom and stamens in the flesh. The fruit contains the memory of the various influences that gave the apple plant its different forms. There is a perfection, a repetition and continual activity in plants.

Have a look at some of the plants around you. What an amazing variety of plant forms there are! When you look at plant forms in this way, can you visualise the activity that has given them life? Can you guess the type of environment that they evolved in? Can you also see the progressive change in form of leaves and petals going from the bottom to the top of the plant stalk as the plant reaches different spheres of activity? The change progresses from the seed cotyledon to leaf, calyx, bud, petals, stamens, ovary, fruit and then back to the seed.

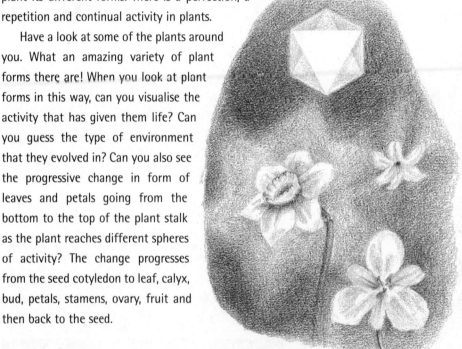

Patterns of three and six: (clockwise from right) hyacinth, native iris, daffodil

The living soil | 3

An essential part of the art of farming is the observation of soil quality. When the biodynamic activity is working well in the soil of the farm, soils of all types have a common look to them. They have a crumbly, nut structure, and the humus content gives a slippery feel when rubbed between finger and thumb. A coarse feel indicates a lack of humus. By running your finger down the length of the profile you can determine the depth to which the humus is in the soil.

On a biodynamic farm, as the years progress, you will find that the soil has this slippery feel to lower and lower depths. The roots also penetrate deeper and deeper. Earthworm castings are found deeper too — down to where the subsoil

Soil improvement after two years of using biodynamic Preparation 500 and biodynamic compost, in a Sri Lankan tea garden. Before (left) and after.

and topsoil meet. The earthworms work to mix the subsoil and topsoil where they adjoin, increasing the depth of the living topsoil layer each year. It is important to observe the degree of mixing of earthworm castings between the subsoil and the topsoil. A good soil on a dairy farm after a few years of Preparation 500 can have over 100 earthworms (*Aporrectodea caliginosa* and *Lumbricus terrestris*) in a cubic foot.

Above: compost worm (*Eisenia foetida*)
Below: earthworm (*Aporrectodea caliginosa*)

Another observation you can make is of the nodules on roots of white clover. On average in a conventionally managed soil they would extend about 2.5cm below the soil surface, but in a good biodynamic soil they can extend down 20cm.

A good fertile living soil will have a strong microbiological life where azobacter and rhizobacter support healthy nodulation on all legume plants, especially where Preparation 500 is being used.

A good biodynamic soil allows roots to penetrate widely, so that they are not cramped and all the root hairs have plenty of room. Observe also that the soil clings persistently to the root hairs. This does not happen in a non-biodynamic soil. In a soil that has been treated with water-soluble fertilisers the roots are contracted and turned in.

Mycorrhizal fungi

A recent new understanding of soil microbiology tells of the benefits to the plant of the mycorrhizal fungi in the soil. These wonderful fungi form a symbiotic relationship with nearly all plants, where the fine hyphal filaments of the fungus attach themselves to the roots of the plant by entering the tissue of the root. These hyphae, which are gossamer thin, being only 1 micron in diameter, can travel long distances to search out nutrients and moisture which are conducted back to the host plant in exchange for carbohydrates. Nearly all plants have this association with mycorrhizal fungi, which are often non-host-specific. The fruiting bodies of the fungi are mushrooms or toadstools, and they can be observed under silver birch, alder and various pines, or in healthy pasture. The hyphae can be observed with a hand-held lens that magnifies 20 times.

The hyphae play a very important role in improving soil structure by developing a crumb structure. Chemical fertiliser will destroy these hyphae.

This fungal phenomenon is very well described in the book *Tales from the Underground* by David W Wolfe, published by Persius Publishing. Rudolf Steiner, in *Agriculture* (Chapter 5, page 104) describes how the biodynamic preparations can support this mycorrhizal activity.

Roots in various soils

In trials conducted at the Agricultural College of Indore in India comparing the effect of biodynamic preparations with that of conventional fertiliser application, there were dramatic contrasts in root development in the different plots. The biodynamic plot showed root development deep into the soil, whereas in chemically treated plots the roots were mainly near the surface.

I have observed the roots under a biodynamic tangelo orchard in the Bay of Plenty, New Zealand, and also under the neighbouring tangelo orchards. The orchard on one side used conventional methods and that on the other side had not been managed at all. Under the orchard managed conventionally the roots were constricted and contracted and there was no soil clinging to the roots when dug up. Under the orchard where nothing had been done there was still a certain amount of root constriction. Under the biodynamic orchard, the roots had moved freely through the soil and the soil clung to the roots when they were dug up.

Soil quality using biodynamic or conventional methods

When you walk on good soil, feel the 'softness' underfoot. When you go to take a soil sample, feel the ease with which the spade goes into the soil. In usual conditions (eg not in a drought) the spade will go easily into a good soil. Observe how quickly the grass recovers after a drought or a prolonged wet period. Recovery will be quicker, the better the condition of the soil.

The ability of the soil to absorb moisture is very important. This ability depends on whether there is a turf mat or thatch. If there is plenty of earthworm activity a turf mat does not build up and rainwater penetrates the soil better.

When I visited a farm in the South Island several years ago, they had had 25mm of rain the previous night, after a three-week drought. We measured the distance that the water had penetrated — 40mm deep. We also looked at the soil on a neighbouring conventional farm and found no water penetration at all. The thatched turf had caused it all to run off.

'Sir...it is like ploughing cotton.' Author Peter Proctor watches ploughing in Gujarat, west India.

There is a farm in Gujarat in western India which has been using all the biodynamic preparations for the last three years. The farmer has been using Preparation 500 and CPP (cowpat pit) since 2001, four times in a year. The ploughman who had been ploughing on this land with a bullock-drawn single-furrow plough for the last twenty years said to the farmer, 'Oh sir, what have you done to the soil to make it so soft. It is like ploughing cotton and my feet no longer get sore.' Such anecdotal stories are backed up by the following research.

Researchers at Massey University in New Zealand made several standard soil-quality measurements on soil from several pairs of neighbouring biodynamic and conventional farms. They measured such things as the bulk density of the soil — the lower the bulk density, the more easily roots can penetrate deeply; the carbon percentage, which is a measure of the amount of soil organic matter; the mineralisable nitrogen, which is the amount of nitrogen available to plants; and the respiration, which measures the amount of soil microbial activity (Reganold *et al.*, 1993).

They found that the biodynamic soils were generally significantly superior to conventionally managed soils in regard to soil structure, friability, aeration and drainage, lower bulk density, higher organic matter content, soil respiration, and mineralisable nitrogen, more earthworms and a deeper topsoil layer.

Tests for water infiltration (Levick, 1991) were carried out in a comparison between biodynamically and conventionally managed orchards in New Zealand. These tests measured how fast water infiltrated and percolated into the earth to be available for the tree roots, by pouring water inside large rings and measuring the speed at which the level went down. In the biodynamic orchards, water soaked away between two and four times as fast as in the conventional orchards.

The vitality and quality of soil can be improved by regular application of:

◎ Preparation 500

◎ compost made with Preparations 502–507

◎ liquid manures made with Preparations 502–507

◎ cowpat pit manure made with Preparations 502–507

and in addition by:

◎ turning in plant material such as green crops and straw

◎ not using chemical fertilisers and pesticides

◎ avoiding soil compaction by machinery or animals, particularly in wet weather

◎ keeping soil covered by pasture, crops or mulch

◎ not destroying the soil structure by poor farming practices such as excessive use of the rotary hoe or cultivation in unsuitable weather (too wet or too dry)

◎ fallowing the land by planting deep-rooting permanent pasture species or using green crops.

These practices will be described in more detail in the following chapters.

Making and using the biodynamic Preparation 500

4

Regular application of Preparation 500 (cowhorn dung) for two to three years begins to give soil the good characteristics discussed in Chapter 3. It takes less time in warm countries.

There is an increase in humus formation, and generally in all microorganisms such as rhizobium (nitrogen-fixing bacteria), phosphate solubilisating bacteria, mycorrhizal fungi, algae, actinomycetes and protozoa. Then there is the increase in the macro-organisms such as nematodes, springtails, mites, ants, millipedes and earthworms, all of which aid the increase of humus formation to a depth of 30cm.

The net result is an improvement in soil crumb structure, an increase in nodulation of legumes, and an increase in the depth of earthworm activity and root penetration. The water penetrability and moisture-holding capacity of the soil will be increased over the years, to a point where some farmers claim at least 25 per cent less irrigation requirement.

Soil pH rises up to a point which is conducive to the support of clover and earthworms in the range of 5.8 to 6.5, then stays at that level. The soil becomes able to allow the plants to express their natural characteristics. This improvement of the soil takes place whether it is clay, peat, sand, volcanic, or silty loam.

Preparation 500 is made by burying cowhorns filled with cow dung in the soil for up to six months during autumn and winter. Cow dung has the amazing ability to attract life such as earthworms to it. Next time you walk across a cow paddock, have a look at all the worms under a partially decomposed cowpat. The cow is an earthly creature with a very strong and thorough digestive process. Some of the forces generated during digestion remain in the dung. Here we are looking at all that emanates from inside the body of the cow — her essential cowness, which Steiner calls 'astrality'. Every farmer and gardener knows the value of animal manure, and in particular cow manure, in improving soil quality.

In India, where the value of cow dung in agriculture is truly recognised, the Indian farmer will tell you that the Goddess of Prosperity lives in cow dung.

The value of the cowhorns, according to Steiner, comes from their ability to hold and ray back continually that animal nature or astrality into the digestive system. This obviously continues to enliven the digestion and resultant dung to a high degree. When the horns are removed from the cow, they still retain their holding and raying back capacity. This gives the horns the ability to absorb the life energies that are in the soil in the winter months during the decomposition of the dung in the horn. Something of the soil life activity is then contained and concentrated in the manure.

For an indication that there are strong growth forces in the earth during the wintertime, just look at the way new white rootlets form and grow on newly planted trees and shrubs. There is no leaf growth during the wintertime, but there is plenty of root growth (see Steiner, *Agriculture*, 1993, p 71).

When Preparation 500 is made it takes on the characteristics of the soil in which it is made. So if the horns are buried in peat soil, the 500 looks black and peaty, in sandy or volcanic soil it is lighter, and in heavy clay soil the 500 has a heavy texture. However, even though it looks different, the 500 still brings about the same beneficial change in whatever soil it is applied to.

Ideally, the 500 should be made in the area where it will be used. Preparation

Burying cowhorns in India.

500 is particularly effective if it is made from locally produced dung on the farm where it will be used, as the forces in each district are slightly different. In New Zealand most farmers use 500 that has been made in Hawke's Bay or Northland. However, I have taken some Hawke's Bay 500 to India and it has worked well there too, in respect to soil structure improvement. In Germany, all biodynamic farmers are required to make their own preparations. In the long term it will be preferable for all biodynamic farmers to do the same.

New Zealand biodynamic farmers and gardeners have been able to benefit from the preparations they can obtain from the BioDynamic Association, which has a quality control based on 20 years' experience. However, after three to four years of experience in biodynamic management, farmers are encouraged to make their own Preparation 500, at the same time keeping a strict appraisal of quality.

Making your own Preparation 500

To begin with this should be done under the guidance of an experienced practitioner or the local biodynamic farm advisor, to ensure that the quality is maintained during all parts of the operation. At any one point the process can go wrong. If you are in any doubt about the quality of your preparation, have it checked by the farm advisor or by your Biodynamic Association (see Appendix 9). If it is not good quality, put it onto the compost heap and obtain some that is. Your land may not be ready yet. The soil may not be fertile enough or the position of the pit may not be right. Try again the next year.

The quality of Preparation 500 can be checked by chromatography, which gives a pictorial image of the strength of the forces present. Several factors contribute to the quality of the preparation, in particular the quality of the dung used and of the soil in which it is placed. Researchers into the science of bio-dynamics in Christchurch, New Zealand have built up an extensive body of experience in making and assessing chromatograph pictures of Preparation 500 (for a description of chromatography see Pfeiffer, 1960).

The experienced biodynamic practitioner learns after a few years to assess the quality of the 500 by the smell, feel and look of it, which is probably the best quality test. Massey University soil scientists have done bacterial respiration tests on 500 which show it to be fifteen times more active than soil and twice as active as earthworm castings (Van Stensil, 1994). The advice given below should enable you to make good 500 yourself.

To make good-quality 500

The dung

The dung must come from healthy milking cows fed on pasture that has been grown using biodynamic methods. Every year of biodynamic management the dung quality improves and so also does the quality of 500 made from it. To make sure the dung is of good quality, choose the best paddock on your farm, one that has a good mixture of grasses and clovers and produces the best milk. Shut the paddock up for about one month, then put the cows on it for two days before the 500 is to be made. Collect the fresh dung from this paddock the day you fill the horns. The dung should be fairly firm, not sloppy, and should have a sweet smell.

Note, using dung from a lactating cow means that the 500 will have the processes of calcium in it, which are complementary to the silica processes present in Preparation 501 (see Chapter 11, Calcium, silica and clay).

Soil quality

It is recommended that horns be buried in a vegetable garden where there has been ongoing sustainable management with biodynamic compost, green manures and preparations of the highest biodynamic quality. It is important that the soil is well drained during winter. Soil quality can be deemed satisfactory if it will grow good winter cabbages or cauliflowers. If there is any doubt about the quality of the soil, then mix with about 50 per cent well-matured biodynamic compost, for the soil that surrounds the horns.

Healthy cows in a healthy paddock, Tukituki Valley, Hawke's Bay.

The cowhorns

The cowhorns used should be as local as possible. In temperate climates the best 500 is made in medium-sized horns. The larger horns that cows grow in hot countries such as India are more suitable for making 500 in those countries.

Small to medium horns, no larger than 5cm in diameter, make the best 500 in New Zealand and other temperate countries. The best and most durable horns are from Jersey, Milking Shorthorn or Friesian cows. Heifer horns can be used but it is generally assumed that mature cow horns would be stronger and contain more forces than heifer horns.

Use cowhorns rather than bullhorns. The cowhorn can be distinguished by having stress rings from calving, being solid at the tip, and being more spiralled.

Horns can be used for several years. Some last up to six years in New Zealand, but some become papery after one year. The durability varies with the breed of cow. If the 500 you make in a horn ends up green, ie the dung has not changed, it hasn't turned. You should throw that cowhorn away as it may have been used too often.

Cowhorn and bullhorn: note the annular calving stress rings and increased spiralling on the cowhorn.

If the horns still contain a bony centre, put them in a pile so that the cartilage holding this centre part rots away; it can then be removed. This will take from two to three weeks.

The pit

The pit should be within the fertile topsoil layer. The horns should not be buried too deep. In *Agriculture*, Steiner said to put the horns 75–150cm down. This would probably be to keep the maturing dung in the horns out of the permafrost zone. In New Zealand, I have found that good results are obtained from digging the pit to 30–40cm. If your topsoil layer is thin, dig out some subsoil and backfill with topsoil from another part of the garden so that the horns can be surrounded with topsoil. The ideal size of the pit is 2 x 4m and up to 40cm deep.

Method

Recently I have had some very good experiences in the making of 500, basically by a simple improvement in the technique of burying the horns.

Always using a mixture of topsoil and a good mature worm-free biodynamic compost, 50 per cent of each well mixed, I virtually plant each horn separately in the pit as I would a cabbage plant. They are 'planted' between 2.5 and 5cm apart, open end down, with the horn being upright and the soil well firmed around as with a cabbage plant. The horns standing upright do not touch one another, as with a cabbage plant, and the pit is backfilled with soil as one goes row by row, so that the horns will not fall over. The horns are totally surrounded by good soil, which gives the manure in the horn a good connection with the soil and with the cosmic forces which will be active in the fertile biodynamic soil.

Burying the horns in this way also obviates the need to throw soil over the horns and having them collapse on top of one another in the pit.

In this way it is possible to make your own 500 in the first year of conversion provided you have very good worm-free compost and good biodynamic cow dung available.

Another reason I prefer to stand the horns upright and placed open end down, is to prevent them becoming saturated during the winter rains or by overwatering if the pit needs watering in a dry winter.

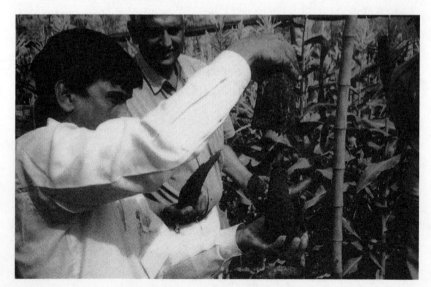

Preparation 500 made in Anand, Gujarat, India.

Make sure the area in which you bury the cow horns has good winter drainage and the water table is not too high. On the other hand, do not choose a pit site that is sandy and dry.

Worms, weeds and wisdom

There are several things that can go wrong in the making of 500. Worms can be a big problem. In a biologically active soil the earthworms will be active and looking for food. There is nothing more frustrating than digging up the pit to find two-thirds of the 500 gone. One year, out of 5000 horns buried, 200 had been completely emptied out by the worms when dug up. To encourage the worms not to work in the horns, put a few barrow loads of raw compost on the top of the pit as a lure.

A further point to note regarding worms is that they may be active during the time the horns are in the ground. Horns should not be left in the ground longer than six months; in hot countries, check the 500 about four months after burying. In other countries, check in early spring to see if it has turned and to make sure the worms are not causing a problem.

Also, watch that weeds or tree roots don't grow into the dung in the horns. The root growth of weeds and trees is very fast in the early spring so do not make the pit near any trees and always keep the 500 pit free of weeds and grasses so that roots will not grow into the manure in the horns.

Time to bury the horns

The horns are generally buried around October in the northern hemisphere, and around April/May in the southern hemisphere. The quality of the 500 might be lower if they are put in later than this. They can then be dug up again in April/May in the northern hemisphere or September/October in the southern hemisphere, which would mean they have spent approximately six months in the ground (see Appendix 3).

You may need to dig the horns up earlier than this if the soil is getting dry; for instance, in Hawke's Bay, New Zealand in 1994 the soil was getting so dry that the horns were dug up in September (early spring). If they had been left longer they would have lost quality. In wetter years they may have to be left longer for the preparation to have turned well.

The burying of cow horns on a farm can be a social occasion for members of the farm, their neighbours or friends.

Preparation 500 in Diu, Gujarat, India.

Lifting the 500

When lifting the 500 in spring, observe its quality. If it is well turned, it should have decomposed and shrunk a bit. It should be slightly loose in the horn and able to be knocked out easily. When you break open the 500 it should have a characteristic sweet smell. You need to learn to recognise the smell of first-class 500. The 500 may take on physical aspects of the soil it is made in, but the smell is always the same. It smells the same all over the world. Microbiologists tell me it is the smell of the actinomycetes, which are often present as small white growths on the 500. No suggestion of the cow-dung smell remains. After a time in storage the sweet smell changes to a very pleasant earthy smell.

Don't be concerned if the 500 has this small white or pink fungus growth or small insects on it. These are visible indications of the life processes.

Using cow hooves, and other experiments

Rudolf Steiner pointed out in *Agriculture* (pp 70–71) that the forces within the cow are rayed back into the digestive system by the hooves as well as the horns. I have experimented with putting dung in hooves. It certainly changed into something that looked like horn Preparation 500, but had a different, slightly stronger smell. This method will need to be well tested before it is recommended for use in mainstream biodynamic management.

Some farmers have experimented with new methods of making 500. Methods may need to vary to suit particular conditions, and it would be a pity to stifle ingenuity. However, the basic principles always apply. Any new method of making 500 would have to be proven conclusively before it could be accepted as a mainstream biodynamic method. If other containers or different dilutions are used, the 500 may be less effective.

Storing of Preparation 500

It is important that the 500 does not dry out as you are lifting it. Keep it under a damp sack all the time. The 500 loses its vitality if exposed to the sun's ultraviolet rays and the drying effects of wind. This can happen very quickly. To store the 500 for later use, place it in a glazed earthenware, glass or enamelled receptacle in a specially made peat-lined box and put it in a cool place, for example a cellar or cool-shed. The lid should be loose-fitting to allow the preparation to breathe. Instead of being lined with peat, the box can be filled with loose peat or sphagnum moss; the receptacle, with a loose-fitting lid, is buried amongst the peat or moss. This method is suitable for storing all the preparations.

Don't forget to look at your 500 regularly, especially during the first two to three months. During this time the preparation undergoes a settling-down process as the biological life converts it into a homogeneous mass; ie the separate pieces of 500 cowhorn dung from out of the horns gradually form together. This is an aerobic process, which is why it is necessary to keep the 500 aerated. It should be kept damp, and if properly stored, should maintain a satisfactory moisture level; but if it seems dry, dampen it with a little rainwater and make sure it is compact enough, by gently pressing it together. If the 500 is getting soggy, gently move it with a garden fork to allow it to dry out a bit. The 500 is fairly self-regulating and it will absorb moisture if necessary when settled down. All the time you should be checking by smell to assess its state.

Well-made and stored 500 should last for up to three years. As previously mentioned, it is important to make sure there is sufficient insulation around it. But don't store it in a plastic bag: chromatography has shown 500 stored in this way to have weakened in strength.

When the 500 settles down you'll notice some exudation, looking like small worm castings. A kind of black dust, like very fine worm castings (probably a bacterial exudate) will appear on the sides of the receptacle. This indicates the 500 is now in a stable state. The settling-down process can take up to four months.

Application of Preparation 500

Preparation 500 should be made up to a solution with water before applying. Bear in mind that the preparation has to be stirred for one hour before applying. For the small garden, this can be done by hand.

Quantities to use

The rate of application is 25g of preparation in 13 litres of water per acre, or 65g in 33 litres per hectare (see Appendix 1). This amount can be reduced proportionally for larger acreages, because of the radiating effect of the 500. A 1000-acre farm may require 12.5g in 13 litres of water per acre. All the preparation should be applied within one hour of stirring, so only mix up the amount you can apply in an hour. This amount depends on the method of application and whether you have friends to help spread the mixed 500.

Multiply the number of acres you can cover in an hour by 13 to find out how many litres of preparation to stir. For example, if you and your friends can walk over 7 acres of land in an hour, then the most preparation to stir at the time is 7 x 13 = 91 litres. If you can cover 50 acres per hour with a tractor and spray rig, then stir 50 x 13 = 650 litres at one time. Or if you are using an aircraft which can cover 200 acres in an hour, stir 200 x 13 = 2600 litres.

Water quality

Use warm rainwater where possible, although unfortunately rainwater can no longer be guaranteed pure. It can become contaminated where there is agricultural spraying in the area. The water should be warmed by the sun or a living flame, such as wood or gas, not by electricity. Don't use water that has been chlorinated or fluoridated. If you use bore or spring water, check it's not contaminated, for example with iron, aluminium or calcium. If you have good quality bore or spring water, leave it in the air for a few days to enliven it prior to using, or run it over a Virbela flowform (see below) for an hour. Remember that bore water may not have seen the light of day for many years. Use a container that will not contaminate the water; an old copper is ideal.

Stirring equipment and how to stir

Always dissolve the cowhorn dung into the water before starting to stir. It will mix quite easily.

For up to one acre of land you can use a bucket. Up to 14 litres can be comfortably stirred by hand with a small stick. Stir while resting your elbows on your knees. To make a good vortex requires a wristy movement. Start slowly at the edge of the bucket and move into the centre, increasing the stirring speed. When a crater appears in the water, break it by stirring in the opposite direction. You can change hands when changing direction, and it is easier to always stir outward, ie with the right hand clockwise and with the left hand anti-clockwise. There should be about three direction changes a minute.

Up to 140 litres, to treat 1–10 acres of land, can be stirred in a 200-litre plastic drum or an oak barrel, using a 1.3–1.6m long, 2.5cm diameter wooden rod, suspended by means of a nylon cord tied to an overhanging branch, door beam or tripod. The rod is tied so that it is swinging 7.5cm above the bottom of the barrel. The rod thus tied takes all the weight and makes the stirring and creating of the vortex relatively easy.

For other stirring methods see Appendix 1.

The stirring process

When you stir 500 into water you create life-giving vortices and a pulsing effect. After stirring for about 30 minutes, you may notice that the water becomes more slippery and viscous and easier to stir. The water has become enlivened by a similar process to that of the growing plant, the rhythm of the expansion to leaf and contraction to seed. In this process you have increased the oxygen content of the water. At the same time you have introduced the cosmic forces that enable the water to become a dynamic carrier of the life energy of the 500 as it is spread over the land.

A similar effect occurs whether the water is stirred in a bucket to form a vertical vortex, or whether a horizontal vortex is formed by passing the water through a Virbela flowform. This can be seen through the heartbeat-like pulsing that you can observe in both methods.

Flowforms

About seven years ago at the New Zealand National Agricultural Field Days in Hamilton, the display of the New Zealand BioDynamic Association featured a Virbela flowform, the Jaerna model. The flowform was working and we put in some cow-dung slurry from a local biodynamic farm as a demonstration of treatment of dairy shed effluent. We were flowing about 160 litres of water with

A Jaerna flowform mixing Preparation 500 in Cromwell.

4 litres of cow dung, which was an approximation of shed effluent. We also added a set of compost Preparations 502–507.

The mixture became very frothy and gave off a typical cow-dung smell. About one hour after the preparations were added, the odour of the dung changed, becoming more sweet, and by the end of the day, about six hours later, the liquid was almost odourless. It occurred to me that the movement of the water cascading down the flowform had had a marked effect on the working of the preparations. This phenomenon was repeated several times over the years, with parallel trials determining the effect with and without the preparations. Without the preparations the smell did not disappear so quickly.

It was after this that the flowforms were used in New Zealand to stir or mix Preparation 500. Farmers using the flowforms have reported very good results, and I have seen the change in soil structure typical of the use of 500 which has happened with hand-stirring or with machine-stirring.

I have pondered a long time over the connection with hand stirring, with the vortex formation and movement of water within the Virbela flowform cascade. Having been a great observer of water movement all my life, watching streams and rivers, the sea around rocks and smooth beaches, I could see in the flowform a very obvious series of vortices formed as the water ran from bowl to bowl.

Also obvious was the pulsing of the water as it dropped into the reservoir tank

A vortex flowform suitable for stirring large quantities of Preparation 500 or mixing liquid manure. It can treat 2500 litres in an hour, which can then be spread by 4WD or helicopter.

at the bottom of the cascade. It is almost at one with the human heartbeat. Also one could observe the rhythmical variation of the water level within each bowl. Sometimes the water would nearly spill over the edge of the bowl, sometimes it would appear quite sluggish. I was reminded of the seventh-wave phenomenon of the sea or the surging of a river around a rock, which is sometimes covered and then exposed as the river flows by.

But what of its connection to what Rudolf Steiner describes in *Agriculture* (p 73) as the method of stirring 500 in a bucket and with the vortex?

Firstly I could relate that with hand-stirring in a bucket, the vortices in effect are built up vertically, one on top of another. In the flowform they are spread out horizontally on a sloping plane.

It was not until I watched an experiment on water phenomena by Rob Dewdney, a water researcher, who demonstrated stirring water in a glass jar and dropping one drop of black ink into the middle of the vortex, that I understood what was happening. The ink did not drop to the bottom or disperse through the liquid, but pulsed up and down, diffusing a little and looking like an archetypal jellyfish. Here was the connection between the two methods of water movement. The cosmic pulse! I could thus relate this pulse rhythm of the flowform to the world's great water rhythm, the rhythm of life, the cosmic pulse, the heartbeat of all living creatures, and so it appears to me entirely appropriate to use the flowform for the stirring of 500.

A large variety of flowforms now exist, allowing a farmer to stir from 250 litres for a smaller farm or market garden up to 2500 litres of Preparation 500 in an hour for a large farm — enough to keep an aircraft busy spreading it.

Frequency, time and place of application

Preparation 500 should be applied at least twice a year — once in spring and once in autumn. The best application times are firstly in autumn, the end of August/ mid September in the northern hemisphere, and in March, April, or even May in warmer areas in the southern hemisphere. Apply again in the early spring (May/early June in the northern hemisphere; September/October in the southern hemisphere) or even later in cooler parts if it has been too wet or windy earlier on. It has been observed that 500 applied in the evening during a very dry spell helps plants to weather the drought.

Always apply 500 in a descending period of the moon rhythm. The New Zealand biodynamic farmer has found this time to be of great benefit in hastening a structure change in the soil. I have noticed that all soil processes are enhanced more quickly if the 500 is sprayed during the fourteen days of the descent of the moon during its path across the ecliptic line. (If you are unfamiliar with these terms refer to the explanations in the New Zealand BioDynamic Association's *BioDynamic Farming and Gardening Calendar*, or Maria Thun's *Working on the Land and the Constellations*. See also Appendix 4, Understanding the planting calendar.) There is an increase of rootlet development during transplanting of seedlings, a more reliable rooting of cuttings, an ease in the cultivation when working up a seedbed both on farm and garden, and a satisfactory harvest of root crops at this time.

Apply the Preparation 500 in the afternoon. 'Afternoon' varies at different times of the year: in early autumn it starts at around 4pm; in late autumn at around 1pm. Similarly, in early spring after 2pm is suitable, but in late spring you should wait until 5pm. I always try to connect the application of the 500 with the inbreathing of the earth towards sunset when the dew falls.

The practice in Europe is to apply 500 only on bare land. However, New Zealand and Australia farmers have found that it is also effective when sprayed on grass — even on long grass. One farmer has found that light drizzle can be helpful when the grass is long.

Having said all that, in India since 2002 we have been spraying Preparation 500 four times a year. This is done twice in the autumn and twice in the spring. The results are very good in that there is a very rapid improvement in soil structure and soil life.

Equipment and methods of distribution

After completion of the stirring the preparation should immediately be applied to the land. A larger area is easier if you have people to help. Use a good hearth brush with natural fibres to apply the preparation over up to 10 acres. Plastic fibres are not satisfactory because they stick together. Walk rhythmically and throw every two steps, with a good tennis backhand stroke (not a golf swing!). A good throw should cover a 10-metre width. If you throw slightly up in the air, the preparation will spread out well. One person can cover one acre in one hour if they walk briskly.

You don't have to get a blanket covering of the preparation. The effect of the droplets of 500 will radiate out to some distance (50–200m) from where it has been consistently applied. One farmer in Northland, New Zealand has never put preparations on one paddock in the middle of his farm, but the paddock is just as good as the surrounding ones where preparations have been applied, because of this radiating effect.

Applying horn manure 500 at the Demeter herb garden, Havelock North.

The Vortex flowform mixes 2500 litres per hour.

On larger areas, you can use a tractor or ute and a spray rig that will spray 20 metres wide. It is possible to cover up to 60 acres of rolling farmland using a 4WD utility truck equipped with an 800-litre tank, $1/2$hp petrol motor, small centrifugal pump and a boom jet nozzle. Go round the circumference of a paddock, then zigzag across the middle.

It is very important to sieve or strain the 500 before spraying as the little particles of fibre in the liquid will block up the jets and cause annoying stoppages. Using pantyhose over the strainer is an effective way of eliminating blockages during the application.

Further details of different spraying methods, for example, use of aircraft, are included in Appendix 1. Laborious as it may sound, there is wonderful satisfaction to be gained from making your own 500 on your own farm and seeing the results that accrue.

Making and using Preparation 501

5

Preparation 501 is also made in cowhorns. The horns are filled with finely powdered quartz and are buried at the opposite time of the year from Preparation 500. The horns are in the earth between spring and autumn, the 'light' time of the year – between March and September/October in the northern hemisphere including India, and between September/October and March/April in the southern hemisphere. The action of 501 is a light process and it appears to me that the light forces are released from the crushed quartz crystals. The extra light is concentrated on the plants, increasing photosynthesis, strengthening the plant and encouraging the development of fruit and seed.

As Preparation 501 works mainly on the leaf activity of the plant, you should start using Preparation 500 first, to establish a structured soil that will support root development. Then after about one year of 500 use, start using 501 on your farm or garden also. Crops can be sprayed once or twice a year, during the growing season. The timing of the application for various crops is important. This is discussed below.

Making the preparation

Preparation 501 is made by taking a well-formed clear quartz crystal (silicon dioxide) and crushing it in a metal structure or pounding it with a hammer or in a mortar and pestle made of iron or steel. Make sure the mortar and pestle have no rust on them. To keep them rust-free, wipe them during the year with a cloth impregnated with vegetable oil.

Silica quartz crystal

The crunched-up silica is now quite powdery and can be put between two sheets of plate glass to grind further, until the silica becomes 'mealy', with a consistency almost of talcum powder. It should feel smooth between finger and thumb. The powder is then made into a slurry with water, and placed in a cowhorn. The horn is left to stand overnight, so that the excess water rises to the top and can be poured off. The preparation will not fall out, as it would if it were dry. The horns are then buried in the same way as for Preparation 500. The horns are buried in spring about the same time as the 500 is dug up; in fact, one could put them in the same pit. Choose a day when the moon is ascending, and not a day of the moon node. Don't forget to mark the site well with stakes and labels.

In autumn the horns are dug up and the 501 can be knocked out. It will be a bit drier than when it went into the horn. Expose it to sunlight to dry it out. Store the 501 in a clean glass jar on a sunny windowsill. Preparation 501 should always be connected to the light and thus never stored in the dark.

Stirring and using 501

Stir the 501 using the vortex method in exactly the same way as for the 500. For large areas it can be mixed in a flowform or stirring machine in similar quantities to the 500. The 501 is then sprayed in a fine mist using a knapsack sprayer, a tractor or 4WD utility vehicle spray rig with a similar nozzle as for the 500, only the pump pressure is 80–100psi. Always use warm water to spray with, as it absorbs the forces better.

You need 1g of Preparation 501 in 13 litres of warm rainwater for each acre. As with the 500, you are not aiming for a blanket spray. The best weather condition is a slight wind; avoid a strong wind. Aim for the mist to hover in the air for a time, then drift over the sprayed crop. It is nice to know that the spray won't have a harmful effect on the neighbours! Tall trees such as mangoes and bananas can be sprayed using a nozzle on the end of a wand.

Time of application

Spray 501 only very early in the morning, at sunrise — usually in spring. 501 can also be sprayed during the summer, for example on a hay crop prior to cutting.

The 501 works on the photosynthesis process in the leaf. It strengthens the plant and the quality of the plant product. Because it is applied to the leaf, be careful that the concentrating of the sunlight does not burn the leaves. In most

Spraying horn silica 501 as a mist using an extension
boom on a knapsack sprayer in Gujarat, India.

parts of New Zealand, where the ozone layer is thin, you need to spray 501 early
in the morning to avoid burning the leaves. This means that you should start
stirring about one hour before sunrise. Some farmers spray at other times, but it's
best to be very familiar with how it works before experimenting.

For maximum effect, the 501 should be applied at the beginning of a plant's
life, at the four-leaf stage – in order to increase the bulk of the plant. Annual
crops can then be sprayed again, just before harvest in the case of a leafy crop, or
after flowering in the case of a fruiting crop.

Fruits

Fruit crops such as apples, peaches, plums and citrus are normally sprayed when
the fruit is about the size of a shelled walnut. Some orchardists spray 501 each
month, including just before bud movement and also after harvest, but not at
flowering. Overspraying can sometimes make the skin of fruit or tomatoes tough.
Every plant has its own particular requirements. Note: spraying fruit trees before
the fruit has reached full size will cause premature ripening.

Grains and hay

If 501 is sprayed halfway through the plant's normal growth, it will tend to bring about a premature flowering, as the 501 very much enhances the light processes which are connected with flowering. This is why you should spray a wheat crop first at the four-leaf stage and a second time after flowering. Also, spray a hay crop just after it has been shut up for hay and then again after flowering, which would be a few days before cutting. Silage could be sprayed after shutting up the paddock and again a few days before the crop is ready to bring in.

Vegetables

Those who are familiar with the workings of the moon through the zodiac will know that spraying of 501 in an ascending period when the moon is in a particular constellation will impart the properties of that constellation to the crop. For example, to enhance a crop of broccoli or cabbage or even pasture, spray when the moon is in Cancer or Scorpio, which are water or leaf constellations. Spray a grain crop when the moon is in Leo, which is a warmth/seed formation period (see Maria Thun, *Working on the Land and the Constellations*).

Spraying 501 when the moon and Saturn are in opposition has been found to be very effective in bringing healing and strengthening qualities. The moon and Saturn are in opposition when they are on opposite sides of the earth. At this period there appears to be a strong balancing effect between the calcium and silica processes (see Chapter 11). The 501 sprayed at this time enhances this healing, strengthening effect. In many cases, this has been found to strengthen the plants against specific fungus attack. There have been regular reports over the years of good results from spraying, for example, powdery mildew in tamarillos, brown rot in peaches, rust on oats, blight on glasshouse tomatoes, and mildew on courgette plants. One New Zealand farmer experimented with growing a courgette plant in a tunnel house and kept it growing and fruiting for 12 months without mildew by spraying monthly with 501 at moon/Saturn opposition.

Preparation 501 is very important for strengthening seed quality. Rudolf Steiner said that 501 would be of considerable benefit to the grains. I have found that spraying 501 on wheat, for instance, makes it very hard, with a high bran content; and it will change soft biscuit wheat into good quality bread wheat.

All the Gramineae family (grass and grains) show in their growth form, in leaf and ear, the typical triangular shape which is the expression of the light forces working within that species (see Wachsmuth, 1932, and Chapter 2 of this book). This triangulation is expressed also in the quartz crystal, so one can assume there is a very strong connection between the Gramineae and silica. The high response of grains to 501 could be because of this connection to the light forces. All the Gramineae family are similarly affected, so hay also responds well. There is a sweet fragrance associated with hay sprayed with 501, and the taste of bread made from wheat that has been so sprayed indicates that the flowering processes have been enhanced.

The sugar content of grapes can be dramatically increased with 501. Sugar content is measured by the Brix level, which on average is about 25. In 1994, a New Zealand grape grower in Gisborne recorded a Brix level of 64 in his grapes, after they had been sprayed with 501. This is believed to be the highest level ever recorded in the world.

Care should be taken when spraying 501. It is a very powerful tool and should always be used with knowledge and experience. Hopefully what has been written here can provide a basis for further discoveries.

Making and using cowhorn clay

In chapter 3 of Steiner's *Agriculture*, he mentions the importance of the effects of clay to mediate between the processes of calcium in the cowhorn dung Preparation 500 and the processes of silica in the cowhorn silica Preparation 501. Many biodynamic practitioners are now using enlivened clay in their preparation-spraying programs. I have used clay that has been put into a cow's horn and buried over the autumn/winter months in exactly the same way and at the same time as my Preparation 500. It is buried in a separate pit. I use the best quality local clay I can find; in my case, bentonite. The clay I have used is smooth, without any grit, and it should be firm and moist. When lifted in the spring it should be slightly crumbly, which indicates a microbial action having taken place. It can then be stored in glass jars in a peat-lined box. I usually spray the clay on the next afternoon after I have sprayed the 500. Use it at the rate of 10g in 13.5 litres of water, stirred for one hour in the afternoon during a descending period, and sprinkled on the land in a similar manner to Preparation 500.

I have noticed quite good results from the winter clay which follows the applications of 500, 501 and the compost preparations (see pp 87 and 123).

Some farmers are also making horn clay at the same time as they make the horn silica Preparation 501. This is stirred and sprayed in the morning.

Making compost, cowpat pits and liquid manures | 6

Compost

Incorporation of well-made compost is important for maintaining and sustaining the humus content, bacterial and fungal life, and earthworm activity of the soil. Compost has two uses: it is an immediate source of nutrients for a crop, and it is also a soil conditioner.

There are two stages to the composting process. First the pile heats up, and there is active and quick initial breakdown of protein with temperatures rising to between 60° and 70°C. This initial breakdown process lasts about six weeks, after which the compost should be turned. Stage 2 is a slower, stable humus formation, and includes worm activity.

Where immediate manuring of a heavy-feeding crop is required, compost can be used before the earthworms have finished maturing it. For improvement or maintenance of soil structure — for example in a vineyard or on pasture — compost is better used in a mature state.

The aim of composting is decomposition with minimal loss of nutrients and the stimulation of beneficial soil organisms. It is not difficult but needs practice and observation.

Materials

Two main types of materials used in compost are:

1 *Nitrogenous* — having high nitrogen content, and including fresh animal manures, fish wastes, green plant materials, kitchen wastes, blood and bonemeal. On their own these tend to putrefy.

2 *Carbonaceous* — more stable and having a high carbon content, and including

hay, straw, shredded prunings, sawdust and other wood waste, dried seaweed, dried maize stalks, dead leaves.

Check your source carefully, as many of the above can be contaminated — for example, wood wastes by anti-sapstain treatments or tanalisation; crop wastes by herbicides; animal manures by drenches.

Blending

The ideal is a homogeneous blend of carbonaceous and nitrogenous ingredients. In practice it is easier to alternate layers — for example, layers of animal manures and fresh green materials interspersed with straw, wood chips, shredded wood and so on. A good idea in making any heap is to aim for 25 per cent animal manure content. If you have less manure available make what you have into a slurry and water each layer with it. I think it important to put some form of animal manure — say cow manure as a slurry, or blood and bone — on the layers of carbonaceous material to supply nitrogen for the growth of the bacteria which will break down this material.

The layers of plant material should be 15–25cm thick and those of animal manure no more than 7cm.

Moisture

Moisture levels should be even throughout. If necessary, add water during construction — not after it has been built, as this can make the heap too wet. It is a good idea to have an open water tank in which dry material such as straw can be well moistened. Squeeze a handful of material — it should be like a moist sponge, where water can just be squeezed out.

Air

An adequate but not excessive supply of oxygen is essential to encourage aerobic bacteria. Too loose a heap, with too much air, will work vigorously for a short time, release ammonia and then become dry and inactive, and causes that white, dry, powder-like fungus. Too firm a heap, with insufficient air, will smell putrid and sour — like the bottom of a swamp. An inverted V-shaped tunnel from layers of a hay bale or from tied bundles of twigs running the length of the heap will help bring in sufficient air.

The first layer should be made of hay or straw, but not too firm or compressed, as it would be if made from nitrogenous materials. Layers of loose, dry, stable manure create areas through which the essential microorganisms and worms cannot penetrate, so these need to be moistened, consolidated and limited in thickness.

Warmth

The optimum temperature results from the right balance of water, air and material. As the heat is produced primarily from the breakdown of the nitrogenous materials, too much of these will make it over-hot, causing nutrient loss to the air, or stopping the breakdown process.

Too much water and insufficient nitrogenous material makes for a cold heap that leaches out nutrients, while a dry one heats up for a short time and then becomes cold and inactive. The aim is to get the heap heating up vigorously within two to three days and then gradually cooling over some weeks. Turning after about six weeks will restimulate the warmth process, but less intensely and for a shorter period of time. The heap should reach between 60° and 70°C.

Size, shape and situation

The heap should be formed in a windrow not wider than 2m at the base and 1.5m high. It may be as long as available material allows. Heaps of different dimensions can create problems: too big a heap can exclude air and the breakdown can be anaerobic; a heap that is too small will dry out.

The composting yard of an Assam tea garden. There is approximately 5 cu m per windrow.

The site should be shaded from the wind and direct sunlight by trees such as silver birch, neem, alder, hazel, kowhai or New Zealand beech. Avoid trees with hungry roots such as macrocarpa, pine, acacia, willow or poplar. A permanent site will encourage build-up of desirable organisms, bacteria, fungi and earthworms in the soil beneath, which will move quickly into new heaps.

The commercial farmer also needs to allow room to move machinery such as a front-end loader that will be used in making and spreading the compost.

Minerals in the compost

Lime: Calcium hydroxide, also known as hydrated lime or slaked lime, should be sprinkled on any freshly cut green material or kitchen waste, as one puts sugar over porridge. Lime of any sort should not come into contact with animal manure as this leads to rapid breakdown and a loss of nitrogen. Hydrated lime is used in preference to agricultural lime because of its very active nature.

Rock phosphate: Where there is a deficiency of phosphorus, rock phosphate can be used in the heap. The bacterial action will help solubilise the phosphorus. It can be used at the rate of 100kg in 20 cubic metres of compost, and the compost used according to your phosphate requirement. Check the cadmium level: use a rock phosphate that has low cadmium — less than 20 parts per million.

Turning compost.

Other substances

Blood and bone or dried bone should be put through the compost heap rather than spread directly onto the soil.

Rock dusts: Depending on their nature these will, on breaking down into fine particles, add a clay content to the compost which will be beneficial to sandy soil.

Seaweed meal can be added to the compost at the rate of 25kg to 20 cubic metres.

Biodynamic preparations

The biodynamic compost preparations are inserted into the heap at the rate of one set of Preparations 502–507 per 5 cubic metres (see Chapter 7), bringing about an order and balance in the decomposition of the compost material. Likewise, when used on the soil, this compost will enable balanced plant growth. With good biodynamic compost we can add a much more varied and rich microbiological life to the soil, which can help combat many soil-borne pathogens.

Covering

Some protection may be needed from the elements. In high rainfall areas cover the heap with something that will shed the rain: for instance, a thatch made with a thick covering of straw, sheets of corrugated iron, or old carpet. Using black plastic or polythene is not advisable unless it is possible to allow the heap to breathe by draping it over a wooden frame.

In dry areas, build the heap in the shade and plaster it over with mud or cow manure, or cover with straw or large leaves to keep moisture in. Check the moisture content frequently and water if necessary.

Turning

The heap should be turned after about six weeks, and corrective measures taken if necessary – such as adding water if it has dried out. The turning process will bring the outside to the centre and vice versa, so an even breakdown will be achieved throughout.

Rate of use

In a market garden, use 20m^3 of finished compost per acre per year. On vineyards and orchards aim to use between 5m^3 and 10m^3 per acre. One cubic metre is a windrow 2m wide at the base, 1.5m high and 1m long, at the time of building.

Cowpat pit

The concept of the cowpat pit has arisen from Maria Thun's development of what she has termed 'barrel compost'. Maria Thun described this compost many years ago as a method of composting cow dung using the biodynamic preparations to assist in the fermentation process. Cow dung is first mixed with powdered egg-shell and also basalt dust, and is put into a wooden barrel that is half buried in the soil. The biodynamic Preparations 502–507 are then put into the dung and the barrel is covered with a moist hessian sack, making sure the barrel is kept cool and the dung does not dry out. After four to six months the cow dung in the barrel has turned into compost and can be used to bring the qualities of the biodynamic preparations into the soil, and in many ways on the farm or in the garden as a soil inoculant or a foliar feed.

In a country such as India where the cow is highly venerated and the fertility quality of the cow dung is recognised, it is hardly surprising that farmers have taken hold of the concept of barrel compost with great enthusiasm. The name 'cowpat pit' was coined in India, but it is now widely known by the abbreviation CPP, not only in India but in many countries where biodynamic agriculture is being carried out. However, the Australian biodynamic association calls it 'manure concentrate'.

From fungal and bacterial plate tests of the CPP, it appears there is a wide range of colonies or families of fungi and bacteria that have proliferated during the fermentation of the original cow dung material, and also from what has been gained from the biodynamic Preparations 502–507. It makes sense that the quality of the CPP will depend very much on the quality of the original cow dung, and in particular on what type of fodder the cows have been eating. Obviously if the milk that cows produce from eating good-quality grass, grown biodynamically, can be made into superb-tasting yoghurt, quark or cheese, the dung from such grass will also be not superb tasting, but of a superb aroma that will make very good CPP. This is something that the discerning farmer can gradually learn to recognise — relating dung aroma to dung quality to grass quality and then soil quality.

The Indian farmers have developed this biodynamic activity to a high degree since 1994, and by 2002 large amounts of CPP were being made and used through-out India, and also supplied to farmers converting to biodynamics.

The pits have an inside measurement of 90cm by 60cm, and are 30cm deep, and the sides are only lined with brick. The bottom of the pit is left as bare earth.

The bricks are a good medium for the walls of the pit since they absorb moisture, and can be watered, which will keep the dung from drying out.

A clean hessian sack or gunny bag, without coloured markings, is placed over the dung and kept moist, again to stop the dung from drying out. The pits are made in series of up to 100 pits in a group, with a central path between two double rows.

In many cases the pits are mostly situated within shade houses, which are usually roofed with coconut fronds. This keeps the pits cool in the hot season and stops the dung drying out, and provides shelter against the heavy monsoon rains during July to August/September or October, depending on which part of the continent they are in.

Method

The method of making the CPP is very much the same in New Zealand or Australia.

- Gather 60kg of cow dung, from cows preferably fed on biodynamically grown fodder. No concentrates or grains should be fed to the cows for two to three days before collecting the dung. I have found that the dung should be firm as this facilitates the breakdown processes.

- The dung is mixed with 200g of powdered eggshell (heat the eggshells in a hot oven for ten minutes to aid the grinding of the shell into powder) and 300g of powdered basalt dust.

- The mixing of the dung is important to aerate it, and you will notice that the consistency will change. Mix for at least 15 minutes; some farmers mix for one hour.

- When filling the pits, make sure they are not filled more than a brick and a half deep (12cm) as the deeper the dung is in the pit the longer it will take to break down.

- Smooth off the top of the dung.

- Insert one set of Preparations 502–506. Make five holes about 3cm deep in the top of the dung, and insert one portion of each preparation into each hole. Cover over the holes. The valerian Preparation 507 is mixed with water. Half of the 507 liquid is poured into a hole in the dung, while the rest is sprinkled over the dung and the bricks and also over the hessian sack.

- ◎ Only a small amount of water is needed for the valerian Preparation 507 so you can potentise the one portion of valerian liquid in half a litre of water using a 2-litre bottle. Hold the bottle horizontally at shoulder height and move it firmly back and forth rhythmically for two and a half minutes. This method is better for the small amount of liquid required for a CPP, rather than stirring 4 litres of liquid, the amount needed, for instance, over a 5m compost heap.

- ◎ After four weeks aerate the dung by turning it with a fork. Smooth it out again afterwards.

- ◎ Thereafter, turn each week. This will speed up the breakdown process.

In India it is possible to have good CPP in three months. In New Zealand or Australia it takes four to five months depending on the temperature.

- ◎ The recovery rate is about 40kg of CPP from 60kg of firm dung.

- ◎ When ready the CPP will be well broken down, with a good humus content. It will have a good earthy smell. It can be used straight away, or stored in a cool place similar to the way Preparation 500 is stored.

- ◎ The empty pits can then be refilled.

How to use

The rate of use is 1kg in 40 litres of water per acre. This means one CPP could be enough to cover 40 acres. It should be stirred for 15 minutes before using, and sprinkled or sprayed over the land.

If it is to be sprayed onto trees or foliage it should first be strained through a fine mesh.

For larger areas, the greater amount of liquid can be stirred in a 200-litre drum with the tripod stirring arrangement, or with the Verbela flowform.

Uses of CPP

As pointed out above, well-made CPP has within it all the energies associated with the biodynamic Preparations 502–507. It will also contain a wide range of beneficial fungi, bacteria and growth-promoting hormones, which can be very helpful in many areas of agriculture and horticulture. CPP can be used in the following ways.

◉ Use CPP in conjunction with stirring Preparation 500. Add 100g of CPP per acre to the stirring for the last 15 minutes as a method of getting the effects of the 502–507 over the land.

◉ Use as a soil inoculant over land being converted to organic management.

◉ Use as a foliar feed on all crops at all stages except close to harvest. It can be sprayed every seven or 14 days. It is best sprayed in the evenings. Excellent for paddy (rice), potatoes, lucerne, etc.

Cowpat pits in Gujarat, India.

- Use on the soil around all fruit trees as a soil inoculant or soil conditioner. In India, for instance, it is used around plantation crops such as mangoes, bananas, papaya, tea, coffee and sugar cane, and in New Zealand or Australia on apples, stonefruits, grapes and all berries. Use before any mulching is applied around the trees.

- Use as a foliar feed on all fruit trees and plantation crops. This will strengthen the plants against possible fungus or insect attack. Apply every 14 days before and after flowering.

- It can be used as a tree paste on the bark of fruit trees to strengthen the bark and the tree against fungus and insect attacks. It can be diluted for this purpose. This can bring the good soil microorganisms up onto the tree.

- Use to dip the roots of all young trees, shrubs and grapes prior to planting.

- Use to soak seeds prior to sowing. Soak for 30 minutes, dry off, and sow immediately.

- Use to dip seed potatoes before planting. Dip the potatoes and dry them before planting. This seems to protect the potato against blight.

- Soak cuttings overnight prior to planting. This seems to assist root development.

- Use as one component of the sequence of biodynamic sprays of 500, 501, 502–507 and 508, which is used to bring the effects of all the preparations onto the land over a short period. This seems to give strength and quality to the plants.

- CPP can be used to inoculate compost heaps where there is a shortage of biodynamic preparations. Use 1kg of CPP in 40 litres of water for each 5 metres of compost, and pour into holes along the top of the heap.

Liquid fish manure

Fish waste can be made into a manure in a similar manner to other organic wastes. Sources of material vary from fish processing plants to game fishing clubs. It is also possible to combine recreation with work, and use the leftovers from the holiday fishing season.

Some biodynamic farmers make a surplus, and supply fish fertiliser to newcomers, who usually need it sooner than the seven months it takes to make.

A 200-litre plastic drum of fish concentrate – at the rate of 1 litre of fish concentrate in 40 litres of water per acre – will do one application over an area up to 180 acres. For a bigger farm, you'll need bigger, non-corrosive vats – stainless steel, concrete or plastic water tanks. Make liquid fish manure in a similar way to other liquid manure, but add compost preparations twice, at the same rate – that is, one set per 200 litres (44 gallons) at the beginning, and one set per 200 litres about three months later.

Caution: Your family may not want to have much to do with you if you have been stirring the fish fertiliser – the smell can be very strong.

Preparation

The method described below is one developed successfully by John Pearce, on his farm at South Head, Kaipara Harbour, on the west coast of New Zealand.

Use a 200–2000 litre non-corrosive container to dissolve the fish. Suitable containers may be old stainless steel milk vats, concrete water tanks, or even a plastic drum.

Before filling the tank with fish, it would be a good idea to set in place some form of filter inside the tank. This can be achieved using a length of perforated Novaflow plastic pipe, connected to the outlet on the inside of the tank and arranged into an upright position. This will sieve out the scales and bones from the broken-down liquid.

Fill with fish, any you can get. An excellent product has been achieved using shark and stingray that have been sliced up or minced. However, fish heads and frames will also make a reasonable product. Cover the fish with rainwater and add Preparations 502–507. Add these at the rate of 10 sets for 2000 litres. Further preparations in the same proportions can be added approximately three months later. (See Chapter 7 for application methods of preparations.)

The brew can be regularly stirred after a month. At about three months it will be cloudy grey, but when ready to use, after about seven months, it is of a clear golden colour and the hydrogen sulphide smell will have started to disperse. Note: it is a good idea to place the tanks well away from buildings because of this unpleasant sulphurous smell.

The use of Virbela flowforms, through which the fertiliser is circulated during the latter stages of the process, has been found to considerably enhance the breakdown. Pass the liquid through for 10 minutes before application.

Application

Fish fertiliser made the biodynamic way can be applied at the rate of 1–2 litres in 40 litres (or 2–4 pints in 10 gallons) per acre. If more concentrated, it may damage foliage. It can also be added to Preparation 500 towards the end of the stirring process.

This fertiliser can be applied at least three times a year, and is very effective as a tonic on pasture, vegetables and fruit trees. It is a valuable source of trace elements, and to a certain extent, a stimulus in the nitrogen processes. Its use is also an excellent way of ensuring the full range of preparations are incorporated into the soil.

Caution: do not use close to harvest, as the crop may be tainted by the odour of the fish fertiliser.

Liquid plant manure from seaweed and weeds

Pfeiffer, in *Soil Fertility, Renewal and Preservation* (1983), talks about plant dynamics, and how the predominant weed is able to supply the soil needs, particularly in degraded soils. In New Zealand, for example, thistle supplies copper and yarrow brings selenium. Seaweed liquid manure supplies a wide range of trace elements.

Liquid plant fertilisers act as a valuable tonic for pasture, vegetables and fruit trees. Use of these fertilisers is an excellent way of ensuring a full range of preparations are incorporated into the soil. They also boost trace elements and, to a certain extent, potash.

Preparation of seaweed

Use a 200-litre non-corrosive container to dissolve approximately 12kg of powdered seaweed or kelp. Fresh minced or ground-up seaweed is also suitable, but should be used in a quantity to half-fill the container before the addition of water. Use rainwater as this contains no mineral impurities which may inhibit the fermentation process.

Warm a quantity of water to 30°C to make the initial solution. This can be topped with cold rainwater. Add Preparations 502–507 as described for liquid fish manure (above). Stand the container in a warm place as this enhances fermentation. The liquid should be agitated at least once or twice a week for aeration and should be ready in approximately two months, when the liquid will be sweet-smelling and of a clear brown colour. It will be necessary to strain the liquid before using. It should also be noted that when the first liquid is taken off it will be possible to add more rainwater and dissolve more of the seaweed that has been left.

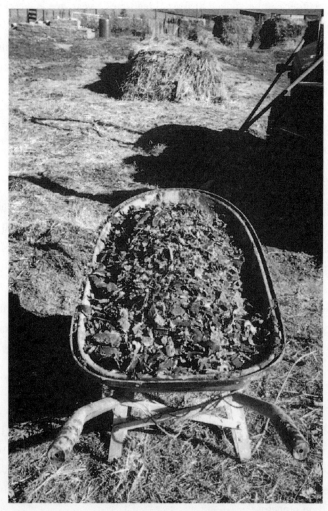

Shredded seaweed for making liquid manure. One barrowload is enough to fill two 200-litre drums of liquid.

Shredding dried kelp for making liquid manure.

Application

Apply at the rate of 4 litres of concentrate in 40 litres of water per acre. This seaweed fertiliser can be applied at least three times a year.

Weeds

Liquid plant manure can be made in the same way from weeds such as thistles, ragwort, or nettles. Shredded legume plants also make a good liquid fertiliser. Fill a drum with the weed and cover with water. Do not mix the weed species, as this seems to interfere with the breakdown. Apply at a similar rate to seaweed liquid manure.

Making and using compost Preparations 502–507 and Preparation 508

7

Rudolf Steiner advised that all the compost Preparations 502–507 should be used in a compost heap. Each brings a particular activity. Some of these preparations take more time and trouble than does 500 but are very satisfying to make. A few New Zealand farmers make their own compost preparations. The main difficulties are in growing and collecting sufficient herbs and in getting the animal parts.

Whether you make your own preparations or buy them, continue to look after them carefully in storage. Check the jars or preparations weekly. If one is drying out, add a very little rainwater. The yarrow preparation is one that is particularly likely to dry out. When picking and drying preparation flowers or foliage, it is important not to dry any of the different plants on the same tray.

The different preparations have different properties. For instance, the stag's bladder Preparation 502 is always loose and dry, while the chamomile Preparation 503 is generally humus-like but can become wet and tacky. You need to look at the compost preparations every day after digging them out, until they reach a stable state.

All these preparations should be made in a descending period of the moon, except for the valerian Preparation 507, for which the flowers and foliage are best gathered on an air/light day.

Preparation 502

Yarrow — Achillea millifolium

This preparation brings in light forces to the soil in the form of potassium and sulphur. Rudolf Steiner describes yarrow as a miracle of creation, particularly with its connection to sulphur and also to potassium. Yarrow is connected to the planet Venus, which is also connected to the kidney.

Yarrow

The yarrow plant grows in waste places on poor soils. Yarrow plants are delicate-looking, but to my eye, beautifully balanced. The roots are mainly at the surface: they are not deeply attached to the earth. You can feel by the feathery lightness of the leaf how the yarrow is strongly connected to the light forces. The leaves have a reduced, flower-like gesture. Yarrow's main feature is its white, composite flowers, which are connected by light forces with Venus. Each flower is like a little chalice – a receptacle for receiving the beneficence of the cosmos.

This connection with the cosmic forces, one imagines, enables the yarrow to concentrate many trace elements. It is a wonderful example of what Pfeiffer (1983) has described as plant dynamics. Yarrow has been found to contain a measurable amount of potassium and selenium even when the soil in which it grows lacks these minerals. In 1985 in Reporoa, New Zealand, liquid manure was made from yarrow plants growing on land where soil tests had showed deficiency of potassium and total absence of selenium. Analysis showed the liquid manure to contain measurable amounts of these minerals.

The flowers are put into a stag's bladder, which can be obtained from a hunter or from a deer abattoir. The stag is particularly connected to the cosmos through its antlers and urinary system. If you look carefully at the stag's antlers, you can see that they have a form similar to that of the yarrow plant, particularly the leaf. A stag is a very nervous animal, and very difficult to approach. Its fluid movement, along with its soft, sensitive eyes, indicate a strong connection to the cosmos. Rudolf Steiner points out that it is through the bladder that this connection is made, and that the bladder of the stag is a reflection of the starry heavens (*Agriculture*, pp 94–96).

Making the preparation

If the yarrow does not flower early enough to use fresh, you will need to pick the flowers in summer or autumn and dry them for use the next spring. Simply cut the flower stalks and dry them on hessian racks, or tie and hang them up in bunches in an airy shed to dry. In the following spring fill the stag's bladder with the flowers which have been cut off the stems with a pair of scissors. If the flowers are too dry, gather some fresh yarrow leaves and make them into a juice with a mortar and pestle and use this juice to moisten the flowers.

If the bladder is fresh and soft, it can be filled through the top using a funnel. A dried bladder can be moistened and also filled from the top. Alternatively, make a small slit in the bottom of the bladder and carefully put in the flowers, and then stitch up the slit. This is so that the bladder is 'waterproof' (when it is hanging up outside), so it does not become waterlogged during any rain, which would tend to make the flowers go mouldy. Do not fill the bladder too tight. Hang the bladder in a tree, on the sunny side, well out of the reach of dogs. The bladder should be exposed to the same weather conditions as will affect your farm during spring and summer.

In the autumn take the bladder down and bury it in soil of a similar quality and at the same time as you bury the cowhorns for Preparation 500.

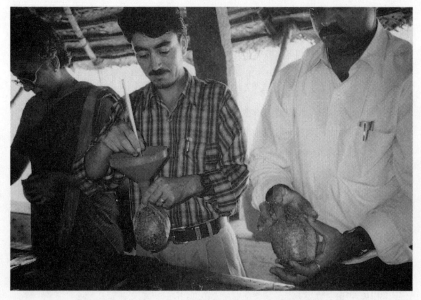

Filling stag bladders with yarrow flowers to make Preparation 502.

Stag bladders hanging in silver birch (Venus) tree in summer.

Put the bladder into a 25cm earthenware flower pot, surrounded by good soil with a mixture of 50 per cent well-matured biodynamic compost and soil. Place soil in the pot to surround the preparation; it can then buried in a 40cm hole, well marked and labelled. See notes on burying preparations later in this chapter.

Retrieving the preparation

When you dig up the preparation, the bladder will have rotted but the yarrow flowers will still be there in a round brown ball. Lift this out carefully and store it in a glass jar with a loose-fitting lid, and put it in a storage box, as described for Preparation 500.

The yarrow preparation never actually forms into humus – you can still see the structure of the flowers in it. As the nature of the 502 is quite loose, it can tend to dry out rather quickly. Press it down a little and firm it in the jar to maintain its moisture. If it does look a little dry you can always add a teaspoon or two of rainwater. Dry preparations will lose their strength.

Preparation 503

Chamomile — Matricaria chamomilla

This preparation promotes a good break-down of the proteins in the compost to humic plant nutrients, and prevents the protein breaking down to ammonia which would be lost to the atmosphere. Most of this ammonia will be converted into the stable form of nitrogen through the humus-forming process. The preparation also brings calcium. The chamomile flower shows a delicate perfection of form.

Chamomile

Preparation 503 is made from the flowers of the German chamomile, not from the Roman or Italian chamomile (*Chamaemelum nobile*, or stinking mayweed, as it is also known). To check that you are growing the German version, cut open the cone on which the little yellow flowers are found. It should be hollow inside, whereas that of the Roman chamomile is solid. To grow your own chamomile, if there are none self-sown, you should sow the seeds in autumn and pick the flowers in early summer.

This plant is an annual and dries off after midsummer. It has a mercurial quality and tends to pop up in different places each year. Chamomile used to be used for preserving meat, well before the days of refrigerators; it prevents putrefaction by holding in the life forces. Chamomile is also used medicinally, particularly for digestion, and also for its calming effect.

Picking the flowers

The chamomile flowers should be picked in the morning before 10am, when the flower petals are horizontal. In the very early morning while the dew is on them the petals hang downwards. The young flowers only should be picked — their centres are slightly pyramidal and greenish, and they have a ring of pollen-bearing stamens at the base of the cone. When the cone is spherical and yellow, the flowers are too old to be of much value. You may find it easier to pick the flowers with a comb.

Drying the flowers is quite important. Spread out the freshly picked flowers on a hessian frame in a warm, shady, airy place (not in direct sunlight). Move them daily until they look dry. Then to dry them off completely, place them in a hot-water cupboard. If the little flowers have any moisture in them at all they will go mouldy in storage. Well-dried chamomile flowers have a beautiful fragrance. When they are crisp, store them in a brown paper bag or glass jar in an airy cupboard. Watch that mice or moths don't spoil them.

Making the preparation

To make the preparation, you need fresh cow's intestines, which can be obtained from an abattoir or a home-kill butcher. Stuff the flowers inside them to make long sausages. I always use a wide-stemmed funnel to fill the intestine with the flowers. Cut the intestines into lengths of 25–40cm. Run them between forefinger and thumb to take out some of the partially digested contents. Then tie one end of the intestine. Pull the open end of the intestine over the funnel stem. Put a small amount of dried flowers into the funnel at a time, and poke the flowers into the intestine with a rounded wooden stick (eg the end of a wooden spoon). Do not pack the flowers too tight. When the intestine is full, tie the end with string. You will notice that any unpleasant smell associated with ageing intestines and warm weather quickly disappears when they come in contact with the chamomile flowers.

Burying the preparation

The preparation should be buried in the autumn. To prevent dogs digging up the preparation, you may have to put a barrier over the area.

The chamomile preparation is the most difficult to recover, as it breaks down completely and is not easy to locate. Earthworms are very attracted to chamomile and will incorporate it into the surrounding soil. I have lost much of this preparation over the years.

To enable you to recover the preparation easily in the spring, put the sausages in a large unglazed earthenware flower pot 30cm in diameter and bury the pot in the earth. You will have surrounded the sausages with soil within the flower pot. As the earthenware pot is unglazed, it will allow all the earth processes to travel through to the sausages. Alternatively, you could put the sausages in a 'sandwich' of sphagnum moss in the soil and mark its position with pegs (see the making of the nettle preparation below).

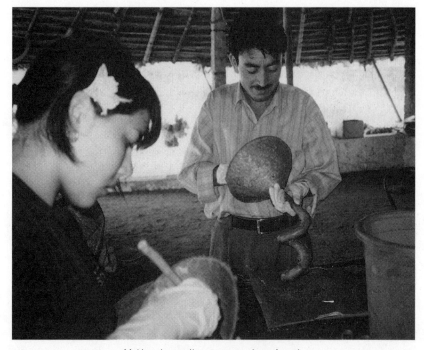

Making chamomile sausages using a funnel.

Preparation 503 being put into a flower pot prior to being surrounded by soil and compost.

Flower pots containing Preparation 503 being buried.

Retrieving the preparation

Lift in the early spring before any earthworms can remove it (they will also come into the flower pot). All the other preparations can be dug up in spring except the nettle, which is buried for 12 months.

Preparation 504

Stinging nettle — Urtica dioica

Nettles show strength and uprightness and perfection of form. Their form, particularly that of the stings, is shaped by silica. The strength of the sting is an important indication of the value of the nettle in making Preparation 504.

Nettle

According to Steiner the nettle is a plant with unique healing qualities for both humans and plants. If you sketch the nettle plant and draw a line to connect up the nodal points or the axils of each leaf, you find the double spiral form of the spiritual staff of Mercury — the medical sign.

The forces of Mars that influence nettles bring iron, magnesium and other minerals, such as sulphur. These forces also have an iron-regulating effect. Many soils throughout the world contain large amounts of iron, which cements the particles together to form what is known as an iron pan. The nettle preparation helps to break up these soils, releasing the iron.

Use the perennial *Urtica dioica*, not *Urtica urens*, which is an annual with less sting. *U. dioica* is used in human internal medicine. A stinging nettle (*U. parviflora*) has been found in India which would probably make good 504, and it would be interesting to see whether the deadly New Zealand shrub ongaonga (*U. ferox*) would work.

Making the preparation

To make the preparation, harvest the nettles in late spring or early summer, before they flower. Dry the whole plant and keep them until you bury them in the ground in autumn. Stuff the dried plant into a round, unglazed earthenware field tile, 10–15cm in diameter or two unglazed, 15cm-diameter flowerpots, which are butted together when filled. Use a broom handle to firm the plant in the tile, and bury it in good soil in the autumn. Mark it well because the nettle preparation is buried for 12 months, until the following autumn. Alternatively you can dig a pit in which you make a kind of sandwich between sphagnum moss. Put a layer of moss down, then about 30–45cm of nettle well firmed down, with moss on the top. Cover with soil and mark well.

Retrieving the preparation

When dug up, the nettle will have shrunk away to just about 2.5cm of black 'compost' at the bottom of the tile. It will be beautifully colloidal. I usually put the preparation through a sieve to break up the stalks before storing it.

In the sphagnum moss method, the preparation is recovered by scraping off the moss first and then the decomposed nettle. Sieve and store. There should be no problem with it drying out during the settling-down stage.

Preparation 505

Oak bark — Quercus robur

Rudolf Steiner pointed out how important it was to have the right amount of calcium in the soil if the plants were to be healthy and free from disease. He said that calcium brings harmony to the form of the plant and does not allow excesses of rampant growth to develop. This condition often arises when the moon forces are working too strongly during and after a wet period. For the calcium to have a healing effect, according to Steiner, it should be in a living form, and it is of no use if applied to the soil as a mineral.

The bark of the oak acts as an intermediary between the dead and the living. About 2.5–5 per cent of its substance is calcium. The oak

Oak tree and leaf

bark is put into the skull of a domestic animal such as a cow, sheep or goat, and buried in a watery environment such as a swamp, or in a water barrel surrounded by rotting plant material. Steiner does not say why the skull is used in this preparation, but a connection to the skull as a moon vessel can be seen if one studies embryology. In all embryo development, which Steiner points out is a moon-growth process, the skull appears first. Another example of the moon-growth process is seed germination, which is enhanced at the time of the full moon (for discussion of these processes, see Lievegoed, 1951).

Filling sheep skulls with oak bark Preparation 505.

As we are trying to regulate the calcium, we surround the bark in a bony 'container' which is built up from calcium. Placing the skull and the bark in a watery treatment will bring a balancing effect between the moon forces and the calcium.

The oak bark preparation will, over a period of time, raise the pH of the soil without the addition of lime. Agricultural lime applied to the land is made more effective where the oak bark preparation is used, and consequently less lime is required.

The European oak *Quercus robur* is used in temperate climates where it grows. *Q. alba* is used in the United States, and in India one of the evergreen oaks, *Q. dilatata* or *Q. glauca*, is being used.

Making the preparation

The preparation is made in autumn. The oak bark is grated to a fine powder with a rasp, then packed tightly into a domestic animal skull, preferably from a cow, bull or sheep.

All the flesh and brain material should be cleaned off the skull before it is used. In autumn, prepare a barrel of rainwater which is connected to a downpipe, so that the water is flowing in and out. Put plenty of rotting, smelly vegetation (leaves, grass, etc) into the water in the barrel. Place the skull in the barrel amongst the rotting vegetation. You may need to put a heavy stone or brick on top of the skull to stop it floating to the surface.

Alternatively, choose a swampy area of land where there is a small flow of water and bury the skull in a hole at the edge of the swamp. Put rotting vegetable matter in the hole. It is a good idea to put the skull in a wire-netting cage and peg it down in case a flood washes it away.

Retrieving the preparation

When you retrieve the skull in spring, split it to take out the preparation, which you put in a glass jar. It will still be smelly because it is anaerobic. Turn it every day until aerobic activity takes over and it smells quite sweet. This can take up to fourteen days. Do not worry about any white mycelium that grows on it during this time.

Preparation 506

Dandelion — Taraxacum officinale

The dandelion flower belongs to the Compositae family. As a flower of Jupiter, it has a crystalline, silicic, cosmic form in a perfect sphere. Dandelion flowers that have gone to seed show the fluffy 'clock' form. The importance of silica is generally overlooked by conventional science, even though about 40 per cent of the earth's surface is of silica. Steiner points out how 'the silicic acid is needed to draw in the cosmic factor, and a thorough interaction must come about between the silicic acid in the plant and the potassium. We must look for a plant whose own potassium–silicic acid relationship will enable it to impart this power to the manure' (*Agriculture*, p 103).

Dandelion

When making Preparation 506, the dandelion flowers are put in a cow mesentery. The mesentery is the 'skin' that holds all the digestive organs in the body of the cow. It is a very sensitive part of the body, and this sensitivity is imparted to the dandelion flowers during their period of preparation in the earth. Steiner notes that: 'This material can be added to the manure in the same way as before, and it will give the soil the ability to attract just as much silicic acid from the atmosphere and from the cosmos as is needed by the plants' (*Agriculture*, p 103).

Preparation 506 gives the soil a living, ethereal quality with the ability to supply the substances that the plant needs.

Making the preparation

Pick the dandelion flowers early in the morning before the sun is too high and the flowers have opened too fully. The flowers should be about half open, with the middle petals still folded inward like a kind of crown. If the flowers are too open when picked they will become very fluffy when dry; these should be discarded. Dry the flowers and store them in a similar manner as described for chamomile.

Cut off as much fat as possible from the mesentery (which can be obtained from an abattoir or from a home-kill butcher). Pile the flowers onto it and fold the skin to make a tight 'parcel' which you tie up with string. Bury the parcel in the soil at a descending phase of the moon in autumn. Use the earthenware flower pot system as described for the yarrow and chamomile, and mark well. You may need to protect it from being dug up by dogs.

Retrieving the preparation

Dig up the preparation at the same time as you dig up the 500. You will find the mesentery is still intact and not broken down. Cut open the mesentery, remove the bulk of the preparation, scrape any broken-down flowers off the folds of the skin, and store in a glass jar. Preparation 506 should be regularly checked and gently aerated for the first few weeks after lifting to make sure it does not become anaerobic. Leave off the jar lid for the first few weeks.

Steiner suggests, in *Agriculture*, that Preparations 503 and 506 should spend six months hanging in a tree before being buried in the ground in a similar way to the stag's bladder. It is not yet known whether this treatment will make these preparations more effective.

Mesentery from a cow for making dandelion Preparation 506.

Preparation 507

Valerian — Valeriana officinalis

Valerian is a perennial plant which has a beautiful leaf with unusually patterned veins. Its triangular form makes it look almost detached from the earth. This form is an indication of its connection with the light forces. I once accidentally tipped over a bottle of the valerian Preparation 507. When I later discovered it I found the contents had dried in the form of the valerian leaf. This

Valerian

shows how the plant products carry a memory of the plant form.

Valerian concentrates phosphorus, which is a vital constituent of plants, particularly the leaf, as it is involved in attracting the light used in photosynthesis. Preparation 507 stimulates the phosphate process and mobilises the phosphate-activating bacteria in the soil. Notice the connection between phosphorus, which burns with a white light, and the white valerian flowers. The flowers have a beautiful perfume. Valerian also brings the Saturn influence of warmth.

Making the preparation

Valerian grows fairly easily from seed sown in spring or autumn in a seedbox protected from frost. It flowers early in the summer of the following year. Harvest the flowers in an ascending period when the moon is in an air/light constellation (Libra or Gemini). I have noticed that the keeping quality of the preparations is greatly enhanced if they are picked during this period. Grind the flowers with a pestle and mortar. Put them in a jar with four times their volume of distilled water – this makes a 20 per cent solution. Leave the jar on a windowsill for seven days, then filter through a coffee filter. Put the preparation in a bottle, filled to overflowing, then cover to exclude air. Store in a dark cupboard.

Using the preparation

Make up to a 5 per cent solution, then stir one 10ml portion into 13.5 litres of rainwater for 10 minutes before applying. You will need 13.5 litres per 5cu m compost heap. (Note that valerian is not put inside the compost heap like the other preparations. Half of the liquid is poured into two holes on the top of the heap, and the rest is sprinkled around and over the heap. Earthworms are very fond of it.)

The valerian preparation can also be spread over a crop to bring warmth. It raises the soil temperature by 1–2°C, so is very useful to protect sensitive plants from frost. This is particularly useful for avocado growers, who need a constant 14°C temperature for three days for pollination. Make up a 5 per cent solution and stir as above, or put it through a flowform then spread it at the rate of 13 litres per acre. You can also spray this valerian solution on grain to improve germination.

Storage

It is very important to store preparations well. They should be kept cool and moist (not wet) in glazed jars with loose-fitting lids in a peat-lined box or just surrounded by peat. *Never* put them in a refrigerator. They are best kept in a cool shady place, for example under a house or in a cellar.

Application of compost preparations to the compost heap, liquid manure and cowpat pit

Whenever you make a compost heap, liquid manure brew or cowpat pit, finish it by putting the compost preparations in it. They will assist the breaking-down process and make the finished product more effective in the soil or on the plants. Each of the preparations acts like an organ in the human body. They work in balance with each other to organise the life processes.

You need one set of preparations – ie 1g each of preparations 502–506 and 10ml of Preparation 507 – per 5 cubic metres (5 tonnes) of compost heap or per 200 litres of liquid manure. For a cowpat pit made with 60kg (one barrowload) of cow dung you can use up to three sets of the preparations. These quantities are suitable for most conditions. In some European countries, twice this quantity of preparation is used.

In the compost heap

Wrap each solid preparation separately in materials such as dried grass or old compost. Make fairly deep holes spaced out along one side of the compost heap, push each solid preparation into a separate hole and close the hole over well. Then with the valerian, make two holes in the top of the heap, pour one-quarter of the stirred valerian in each hole and close the hole over. Sprinkle the rest of the liquid over and around the heap.

In liquid manure

Wrap each preparation separately in old compost or dried decayed grass and float it on the top of the liquid manure. The 507 is sprinkled on the top of the liquid after being stirred for 5–10 minutes.

In the cowpat pit

The preparations are simply pushed into the manure and the valerian is sprinkled over the top.

For small volumes of valerian, eg when using for the 200 litres of liquid manure or in the cowpat pit, rhythmically shake 10ml of 5 per cent solution in half a litre of water in a 2-litre glass bottle. Shake the bottle horizontally at shoulder height, moving it firmly back and forth rhythmically for two and a half minutes.

Preparation 508

Equisetum — Equisetum arvense

Equisetum

This is one further preparation, which is not applied to the compost heap. Preparation 508 is made from the *Equisetum arvense* or horsetail plant, which grows in swampy wastes in Europe and Australia but is less common in New Zealand.

The equisetum plant has a very high silica content. If you burn it the carbon burns off, leaving a skeleton of silica. The preparation can therefore be used in a similar way to Preparation 501, to reduce excessive water forces around the plants and so reduce the risk of fungal disease. Equisetum does not bring the light forces that 501 does, so will not encourage plants to shoot to seed.

Making the preparation

Harvest the plant in spring and dry it. Add it to rainwater at the rate of 100g per 2 litres of water. Bring it to the boil and let it simmer in a covered pan for 20 minutes, then leave it to stand for two days. Alternatively, you can soak the leaves in cold water for two weeks. The preparation should then have a good smell and be ready to use. Add 18 litres of water and stir as you would be for Preparation 500, for 10 minutes.

(Drs E and L Kolisko researched the effectiveness of different dilutions of equisetum. They found that the best results were obtained using a D5 solution. This is made by adding 10ml of the original solution to 90ml of distilled water, shaking it rhythmically for two and a half minutes then adding 10ml of that solution to 90ml of distilled water and shaking and repeating this procedure a further four times.)

Using the preparation

Spray the diluted preparation on the ground around the plants you want to protect just before stress times, for example just before full moon or perigee, when the moon is closest to the earth. Preparation 508 can be used frequently and it's a good idea to use it as part of your routine maintenance in early spring.

In Australia, Robert Williams found that using the foliage of the mountain sheoak, *Casuarina stricta*, as a substitute for equisetum had good results.

Notes on burying the preparations

The quality of the soil in which all the preparations are buried is very important. Good biodynamic soil will attract cosmic forces which will help the quality of the preparations.

Over the last few years I have been burying the preparations in unglazed earthenware flower pots with good results. Being unglazed allows the moisture and the earth forces to flow freely through the walls of the pots. This method also has the advantage of ease of recovery and there is little worry of losing the preparations to worm damage.

Place the preparations – the yarrow, the chamomile and the dandelion – in a 25cm unglazed earthenware flower pot and surround them with the mixture of good soil with 50 per cent mature, worm-free biodynamic compost. Firm down the soil around the preparation as if you were potting up a pot plant. Bury the pot with the preparation in a pit 40cm deep, lying it down horizontally. Mark each end of the pot with a stake, labelling it with the name and date, and fill in the hole.

If you have two pots of preparations join them together at the wide end when burying (see photo page 73).

The nettle in the clay tile should be buried and surrounded with good soil.

Conversion from a conventional to a biodynamic farm

8

Pastoral farms

To begin to be a successful biodynamic farmer you need first to have good farm management skills. The decision to change from a conventional input-output system to using biodynamic techniques requires courage. You can no longer depend on 'quick fixes' to problems. But you can be reassured that many farmers have already taken this step and have built up successful biodynamic farms.

How does one go about converting a farm that has been managed conventionally to a biodynamic management system?

The same basic management changes will apply whether the farm is a dairy farm, a dry stock farm, an apple or kiwifruit orchard or a market garden. The conversion begins with the soil. You will need to start thinking about how a healthy soil life can be encouraged.

You will be extending your focus from quick growth over one or two years to sustaining the farm fertility for many years into the future. You'll stop working with the water-soluble fertilisers that damage soil structure and start building up the fertility and life of your soil. Stop using all chemical weed control! These chemicals leave undesirable residues in the soil that inhibit the development of an active soil life.

First take stock of your farm and its condition. Look at what plants grow naturally on your farm, such as trees and weeds. They are a good indication of the soil characteristics. A proliferation of hawkbit and buttercups indicates a low soil pH. The number of trees on your farm is also important. A farm needs adequate trees to provide shelter and shade for plants and animals. The trees benefit the environment, providing sustenance particularly for birds and bees. They also help to conserve moisture.

The soil

What is the state of the soil on your farm? Is it open and aerated, containing earthworms and organic matter, or is it hard and compacted and 'dead'? What is the history of chemical inputs? The soil on most farms is likely to be pretty dead after many years of chemicals such as superphosphate, pugging by stock, and driving of heavy machinery over it. Have the soil tested for chemical residues such as DDT, and heavy metals such as cadmium or copper. You can't get Demeter certification for soil containing these substances; however, putting Preparation 500 on will accelerate the breakdown of DDT etc. The effect of the heavy metals can be reduced by increasing the living soil layer.

A soil test for available calcium and phosphorus is helpful, and soil bulk density is a good indication of the quality. Check the soil pH. A low pH, under about 5, reduces the availability of nutrients to plants and the preparations don't work so well.

If your soil test shows no measurable potash either in the topsoil or in the base rock, you will need to add potash — either the potash-rich rock feldspar or as sulphate of potash K_2SO_4. Never use the muriate (chloride of potash), as it contains damaging chlorine. Feldspar or the sulphate should be included in a compost heap or put into liquid manure to enliven it before applying to the land. Steiner recommended a liquid of the poisonous purple foxglove (*Agriculture*, p 248).

Soils in estuarine areas and in some inland areas of Australia have a high salt content. On these soils you need to grow particular plants, such as mallee, which remove the salt. Such plants should always be grown around cropping areas.

The base rock the farm is on affects long-term mineral availability. The soil type and basic structure is also important. A sandy soil will always tend to dry out. You can turn most soils into good soil eventually, but it's better to start at least halfway there!

Don't despair if your soil is shallow and hard. One hill country farmer in the Waikato, New Zealand, started with hard, shallow soil, but after four years of applying biodynamic methods, plant roots on his farm can now penetrate more than a spade-depth down, and you can't even see the subsoil. His farm now looks greener than neighbouring farms, and there are no more slips, because water soaks into the soil instead of running off. The improved soil and pasture allow greater flexibility of grazing management than on surrounding farms.

Water, climate, terrain and situation

Check the farm's drainage, and the availability of good-quality water. The water should not have a high iron content or high lime content.

The farm's terrain, aspect and microclimate are all important. Which direction does the prevailing wind come from? In the southern hemisphere, a gently sloping northeast slope is ideal, particularly for fruit-growing. This aspect gives plentiful sun and less drying effect on the soil than a northwest slope. In the northern hemisphere the slope would need to face south or southeast. A slope is less subject to frost, which tends to collect in a valley.

Proximity to markets, transport and labour are important. What sheds and equipment do you already have? These will need to suit whatever farming projects you have in mind.

Choice of farm enterprises

Your choice of farm enterprises should be based on all these characteristics of your farm that you have identified. Growing crops that are suitable for your particular farm is very important.

Stock

Look at the type of stock carried on the farm. There are three great fertility tools farmers have at their disposal: the first is the cattle beast; the second, legumes (clover, lucerne, vetches) and the third, the farmer's greatest friend, the earthworm. In the case of a mixed farm, half the number of stock units carried on the farm should comprise cattle: their manure has a unique effect on soil fertility.

Begin to reduce the dependence that animals have on chemical drenches and dips by gradually replacing these with, for instance, cider vinegar and garlic drenches (see Appendix 5). It may take up to five years to eliminate the chemical drenches and dips completely in the case of sheep and goats. In the case of cattle, however, chemical drenches and dips can often be eliminated in a much shorter time. If it is necessary to use an allopathic drench, the animals should be put onto a quarantine paddock until the drench is eliminated. This will contain the contaminated dung, which will then not have a harmful effect on the rest of the farm.

On livestock farms stock-licks can provide trace element needs in the short term. It may also be possible to use various weeds to supply trace elements; for example, wing thistles made into a tea and used as a drench can supply needed copper (see Pfeiffer, 1983, chapter 11).

Aim to establish a strong genetic base for your animals. Breed only from the healthy ones. Animal and plant health will improve as the soil becomes more alive from the use of the preparations.

Improving the soil

European plants need a higher soil pH and more phosphorus than do New Zealand native grasses and trees.

Lime

Adding lime to the soil increases both the number of worms and clover growth. You don't need a lot of lime because the Preparation 500 will enhance the calcium process. Lime stimulates soil processes and plant growth initially, but will also burn out the humus.

There are three forms of lime used in agriculture. The first is calcium carbonate, $CaCO_3$, which is known as agricultural lime or limestone rock, and is quarried. This form is ground fine and spread over paddocks. Burnt lime or rock lime, calcium oxide (CaO) is made by burning $CaCO_3$ in a kiln. The third form is called hydrated or slaked lime. This is made by adding water to burnt lime. Hydrated lime, $Ca(OH)_2$, is a very fine powder and is the form recommended for use in compost-making. Note: for liming the soil, do not use dolomite ($Ca(Mg)CO_3$) unless there is a known magnesium deficiency. Overuse of the mineral will increase the magnesium to a degree where it will upset the availability of potassium.

Aim to get the pH up to 5.8–6.5 for pasture of European grasses. An average loamy soil in New Zealand needs 500kg of agricultural lime ($CaCO_3$) per acre, applied in the autumn. Then use Preparation 500 in the autumn and the spring. Lime may not be needed again for several years.

The rate of application of Preparation 500 varies between different countries. In New Zealand we have found 25 g/acre to be effective. In Australia, 25 g/acre is also recommended, and in Germany, 100 g/acre. In New Zealand and Australia, on large farms 250 hectares and over, the amount of Preparation 500 can be reduced to 15g per hectare (6 g/acre). You can get an additional effect from two applications a year, if possible in September and October (March and April in the northern hemisphere). This is more effective than increasing the quantity for one application. Aim to apply it at the descending period of the moon around the time that dew starts to fall in the afternoon. After a while you will become sensitive to when is the best time to apply 500.

Many farmers in New Zealand, Australia and India are applying Preparation 500 four times a year — twice in spring and twice in autumn — with wonderful results, particularly on degraded soils.

The compost preparations are also very important. You need one set for 4 acres each year. You will find that after several applications of these preparations your stock health improves dramatically. However, on sandy soil you don't get much effect until the soil has a good organic matter content.

One way to apply the compost preparations over a large area is in liquid fertiliser. Use seaweed or thistles if these are plentiful, or cow manure. Put your seaweed or other material in a black food-grade polythene drum in a warm, sheltered place. Add the compost preparations as described in Chapter 6.

You can apply the liquid fertiliser with the Preparation 500. Add the liquid fertiliser to the 500 for the last fifteen minutes of stirring. The application rate is 13.5 litres of 500 and 2–3 litres of liquid fertiliser concentrate per acre.

Possibly a better way is to apply the cowpat pit manure with the 500 application. The rate of use is 150g per hectare, mixed with the 500 for the last fifteen minutes of stirring.

Preparation 501 should not be used during the first year, except maybe on a hay or silage paddock. Apply the 501 in the second year, after the first application of 500. Preparation 501 brings a quality to all plants which will improve the taste of the fruit or vegetables and the health of the animals that eat the fodder. The timing of 501 application is important; for instance, use it at the beginning of the growth of the plant and again just before harvesting. Do not use it halfway through pasture growth, for instance, as it will bring on premature flowering of the grasses. Chapter 5 gives detailed instructions on when and how to apply 501.

Sequential spraying of the biodynamic preparations

One very good way to apply all the preparations to land that is being converted to biodynamics is to use 500, 501 and 502–507 in a sequence. The rationale is to get the influences and balancing effect of the preparations working together within a short period of time. The method is:

- in the evening, 500 plus the CPP in which there are the 502–507;

- the following morning, 501;

- that evening, horn clay (see page 51);

- and the next morning, equisetum 508.

I like to time this application so that the 501 is sprayed when the moon is in opposition to Saturn, or in the 48 hours before full moon.

This is a new idea but many farmers, including myself, have tried this out with very good results. Here we have an opportunity to observe the results of these new timings of preparation application, and to tell other biodynamic farmers what we have experienced.

Phosphorus

Phosphorus is also needed for plant growth, particularly leaf formation. The phosphorus is naturally cycled in New Zealand native bush and leaf mould, but is lost when the bush is removed. It does not occur naturally in most soils throughout the world and must therefore be added, to provide a healthy leaf growth. Phosphorus, even when added in a soluble fertiliser, can also become insoluble in a dead soil, and so unavailable to plant life. You'll need to add phosphorus initially, as rock phosphate, which will be solubilised by the bacteria and organic acids in a healthy living soil and made available to the plant. Alternatively, the rock phosphate can be put into a compost heap, where a similar process will take place to make the phosphate available to the plant.

Make sure the rock phosphate does not contain cadmium or other heavy metals, which is likely if it comes from Nauru or from North Carolina in the US.

In some areas of New Zealand which have been treated with a lot of contaminated phosphate, the sheep organs have a high cadmium content. Watch that you are not buying blood and bone fertiliser that comes from such animals. Reeds also take up cadmium, so cadmium can be removed from the soil by growing reeds, then burning them and recovering the cadmium from the ash.

'Sechura' phosphate from Egypt is a good uncontaminated source of phosphorus. It should be applied at the rate of 100kg per acre in spring when there is active grass growth and an active microbiological life in the soil.

Potassium

If potassium is a component of the base rocks of your area, as it is in much of New Zealand, you do not have to add it to the soil. Potassium is present in volcanic and granite rocks at between 2 and 4 per cent.

To help break down the rock and make this potassium available in the soil, use biodynamic compost and CPP to encourage the soil-forming processes as previously described, grow deep-rooted plants and encourage earthworms.

New equipment needed

A new biodynamic practitioner will need an efficient mixing system — either machines or flowforms — with which to stir the biodynamic preparations, and some kind of sprayer to apply them. However, on smaller areas of up to 20 acres, you can stir and apply the preparations by hand. Details of stirring and applying the preparations, and machinery and flowforms that can be used, are given in Appendix 1. The pulsing of water in the flowforms seems particularly important, and I advise putting your liquid fertiliser through the flowforms also (see Chapter 4).

Planetary influences

As you become more confident in your approach to biodynamic management, you will find it useful to acquire a working knowledge of the way the moon and other planetary rhythms affect the whole management system. (See Appendix 4, Understanding the planting calendar; Maria Thun, *Working on the Land and the Constellations* and the New Zealand BioDynamic Association's *BioDynamic Farming and Gardening Calendar.*)

Dairy farms

Much of what has been said in this chapter applies also to dairy farms. Most dairy farms will be pretty dead after years of application of superphosphate and urea. But the farm may have good potential, particularly if it is on pumice, where the soil can be deep and well drained.

Many paddocks on dairy farms in wet areas have suffered from pugging over the years. You need to prevent further pugging by having somewhere to over-winter cattle, where they won't do so much damage to the soil structure. It is not good for the animals to stand on wet ground — they need a covered dry pad or a barn. It is important not to stress your animals. The stocking rate should not be too high — no more than one cow per acre in New Zealand — and you should always have feed ahead of your cows.

You may have some animal health problems during the farm conversion stage. If you use allopathic medicine on a cow, eg drench for bloat, you have to quarantine the cow. After one treatment of penicillin the cow cannot be certified as Demeter for two years. There are homeopathic remedies available. For mastitis you can use garlic (as a drench on an empty stomach) and massage the affected area with Weleda marjoram/melissa ointment in the morning and argentum ointment in the evening. Also drench with marjoram or lemon balm in cider vinegar. A garlic and nasturtium and cider vinegar drench is effective against bloat and it does not taint the milk if given just after milking. Cider vinegar is a good tonic – put 2 litres in the drinking trough each day, or sprinkle it on the hay (see Appendix 5).

Some cows will adapt to the new regime more easily than others. Naturally you would have to give allopathic medicine rather than see an animal suffer, but do not breed from cows that need such medicine, and gradually cull them. I once had a cow that kept getting mastitis in the front right quarter, and its calf also got mastitis in the same quarter. I finally had to cull the cow and calf.

The health of the animals may take two years to improve, but sometimes bloating stops as soon as you start to use 500 on the pastures.

Calves need good management. Suckle them on nurse cows, three per cow. Wean no earlier than three months old; four months is better.

Gradually change the pasture sward to include a wider variety of plant species, for instance deep-rooting plants such as chicory, red clover, lucerne and cocksfoot, which improve the soil structure. This variety of species will bring health to the livestock by means of diversity of diet, and will also bring more minerals into the farm system. A suggested herbal ley mixture is given in Appendix 6. You can increase the number of grass species on your farm by making hay from a herbal ley in which there will be seeds and feeding the hay all round the farm.

Shorthorn cows on a biodynamic farm in Hawke's Bay.

Make sure you have sufficient hay and/or silage. Aim to have two years' supply, because the weather can be uncertain. Establish a rhythm on the farm, for example with preparation- and fodder-making, to make up for vagaries in the weather. Cut the hay and silage when the moon is ascending and in Gemini if possible. Even if it rains it won't spoil, particularly if you applied Preparation 501 during a period when the moon and Saturn were in opposition one week before.

Grow crops for feeding in a dry summer or for making silage. Maize is best, chopped up. A good winter crop is Italian ryegrass and red clover, or vetch oats, rye corn and triticale.

Cowshed effluent

The dung droppings and the urine of cows during the time they are in the milking shed or parlour are a very valuable source of fertility. In New Zealand this waste is often discarded by farmers, who see it as something to be 'got rid of'; usually it is hosed down a drain into a pond. Here it is supposed to go through an oxidation process before it may or may not be spread over the farm.

Some farmers have a large 'sacrifice' paddock near the cowshed onto which the effluent is pumped each day. This results in a wet, soggy paddock and a build-up of nitrogen with resultant unpalatable grass.

The biodynamic farmer will run the effluent over a Virbela flowform for an hour and will add some cowpat pit to introduce the preparations before spreading it onto the land. This will stabilise nitrogen in the liquid.

Another option is to put cowpat pit liquid manure through the flowform for about 20 minutes and introduce this into the effluent pond. This will quickly break down the solid material and it can be spread over the farm after a week.

In both cases the effluent can then be pumped over the farm through a travelling irrigator, or spread with a liquid-manure wagon. In this way the whole farm can be treated. It will take about two years to get over the whole farm. Farmers have reported that cows will go on eating grass immediately after the spreading of the treated effluent. They also report an increase in clover growth; and there have been reports of a decrease in incidents of mastitis.

Some biodynamic farmers collect the solid manure for compost-making, which means there is less effluent to deal with. Farmers in India also collect cow urine for making compost and liquid manure, and also to be used as an insect pest repellant.

Sheep, beef and cropping farms

Ideally a farm should have at least 30 per cent of flat land and you should be able to drive a tractor over most of the farm. A dry area with good drainage is good for wintering cattle and strong clay/silt country is suitable for withstanding summer drought and for cropping. The best location is within 30–40km of saleyards. Check water availability, trees, nutrient status of the soil, fences, gates, woolshed and cattle yards. Do a budget, including all the inputs needed.

The pasture will need less lime and phosphate than a dairy farm. You could apply these and the biodynamic preparations on a section each year as your budget allows. More intensive applications would be needed on cropping areas. On large, hilly areas you may have to apply the preparations from the air. You then apply liquid manure or CPP with the Preparation 500 (see Appendix 1).

The cropping area must be fertile. To grow 1 tonne of wheat you need 40kg of nitrogen. One cattle beast gives 20kg of nitrogen per year, so you would need the build-up from several years' grazing before you can grow a crop. Including legumes in the pasture helps to build up nitrogen, and applying the preparations encourages worm activity and build-up of humus and soil structure. Weeds are a good indicator of how fertile the paddock is: if there are lots of flat weeds such as broad-leaved plantain, hawkbit or cat's ear it is not fertile enough for cropping.

When you buy in stock you must first keep them in a quarantine paddock. Find out what they've been drenched with. Avoid buying stock that have had Ivomectin. (Ivomectin is a synthetic material that is such an efficient internal worm drench that it kills earthworms as well. Its effects last in the dung a number of years, so dung from animals treated with this material will not break down.) Animals take on the certification of the farm after they've been there for two years. Those conceived and born on a Demeter farm can be certified as full Demeter.

Suitable stocking rates will generally be between three and five stock units per acre, depending on the area. Aim to have even numbers of stock units in cattle and sheep. (One adult cattle beast is one stock unit, equivalent to five adult sheep.)

Your aim will be to get the nutrients cycling so that you don't need to add minerals or trace elements; in fact, adding trace elements could upset the balance. Regular application of the biodynamic preparations through the 500 and CPP will ensure that the soil is working biodynamically and ordering the cycling processes.

Of course, some nutrients are lost when products are sold off the farm, but this is mainly carbon. Most minerals are recycled, and are also synthesised by the plants, particularly the weeds.

Most of the calcium in milk does not come from the land, but is synthesised in the cow through eating quality fodder. The calcium in the soil helps the pasture to grow as it basically encourages clover growth through an increase in the nitrogen nodulation of the clovers, and calcium also encourages earthworms, which improves the soil structure.

If the grass is eaten down low at the start of spring, it will take some time to get going. Growing a feed crop to use when grass is in short supply will help prevent overgrazing. But don't let animals onto a crop during wet weather. It's better to turn the crop into silage and feed it out.

After applying biodynamic practices for a few years you'll find your farm will develop into a self-contained entity. The healthiness of the soil, pasture and animals will be evident. It will develop its own individuality.

Conversion from a conventional to a biodynamic farm — orchards and vineyards

9

You may be considering converting an established orchard to bio-dynamic management or planting a new orchard on bare land. If you have a choice, the latter is easier, as you won't know what has been put on the soil of an established orchard.

If you are converting an established orchard, find out whether the varieties of trees that have been planted are suitable for that environment. Some varieties are better suited to biodynamic methods than others; for instance, Gala will always be susceptible to blackspot.

How are the trees grown — espalier or with single leaders? What shelterbelts are there?

Try to find out what chemicals have been used in the past. How compact is the soil? If there is a lot of moss in the spray strip, the soil is badly compacted and it will take at least three years to get it right. You will also need to consider what spraying is being done on neighbouring orchards and how close they are.

Be aware of the frost liability, particularly if you are growing stonefruit. It is better to plant on a slope where the cold air drains down and away than at the bottom of the slope.

Converting an existing pipfruit or stonefruit orchard

The first job is to establish a good herbal ley between the trees (see Appendix 6). You may have to disc up the soil and put in a green crop first. Repeat this for a second year, to get the soil active, before putting in the ley.

The aim is not to have to irrigate the trees, as this prevents the roots from growing properly. Encourage the roots to go deeper with plenty of humus in the soil.

Start making compost at the beginning. You'll need at least 10 tonnes per acre.

You'll also need cows on the property. This is a radical thought but well worth considering. For each five acres of orchard, set aside one acre to run one cow. Cows can be put in a yard at night and the dung collected daily to be used in the compost or for liquid manure. Cows are more useful than poultry: note that raw manure from poultry, if uncomposted, can taint the fruit. Also, the high nitrogen content in the poultry manure can cause rampant soft growth which can be susceptible to fungus and insect attack. If you do decide to keep poultry, geese would be more effective than chickens, as geese eat insects.

Establishing a new pipfruit or stonefruit orchard

Look for a property large enough to include an area to run cattle — not so much for milk production as to provide dung for making compost. Perhaps there will be also room for cropping and you will be able to grow plenty of material for making compost.

Select trees that have a proven record of being disease-resistant in that district. Now that there is a growing demand from Europe for products grown in an environmentally friendly way, researchers in New Zealand have been developing varieties that are resistant to diseases such as blackspot and mildew. There are now about seven promising varieties as a result of crossing varieties such as Braeburn, Gala and Cox's Orange with other Malus species such as crabapple, *Malus floribunda*.

A few New Zealand nurseries, such as Tree Dimension Nursery in Motueka, have old varieties of apple trees. Many of these, such as the russet apples, do not have so much eye appeal but still taste fine.

Shelter

The purpose of shelter is to break up the blasts of wind which will stop the trees growing. Shelter should filter the air rather than stop it with a solid wall of trees. It should not be too dense, and good air movement should be possible at all times. The side facing the sun should be deciduous; the side facing the cold winter winds, where protection is needed, can be more dense, with a mixture of deciduous and evergreen trees. Avoid planting any species with vigorous roots, for example willow. For a list of some species suitable for New Zealand conditions, see 'Shelter' in Chapter 10. All species should be trimmable.

Planting

Plant new trees into cultivated soil, 3–4 metres apart. If they are too close there will be insufficient airflow, which increases the risk of disease. When planting, fill the holes with a mixture of soil and compost, and also spread compost around the trees on the soil surface. The compost should have been made with the compost preparations, as described in Chapter 6.

Keep grass and weeds away from the young trees by mulching with hay or straw, as grass roots seem to inhibit the roots of young fruit trees. The mulch should be spread to at least 1 metre out from the trees, but should not touch the tree stems.

You can grow potatoes between the rows in the first year as a catch crop. Then, in autumn, sow a herbal ley containing chicory, red clover, lucerne and cocksfoot. This can be cut for the first time in spring. The ley will eventually provide a great mulch.

Don't install a drip-type irrigation system, or the tree roots will not grow down deep into the soil. You should not need to water the trees at all, even in very dry areas, if you have, with good biodynamic management, established a structured soil with a high humus content.

Application of the biodynamic preparations on new and established orchards

Spray with Preparation 500 twice in the autumn and twice in the spring in the first year. In the second year, three sprays of 500 should be sufficient. Fruitgrowers in New Zealand may have to keep applying 500 at that rate permanently to combat the effects of the hole in the ozone layer: in some areas, avocados are getting sunburned two months before they are ready for picking.

Equisetum or Preparation 501, applied at the perigee and when the moon and Saturn are in opposition, help to suppress fungal growth. If they are also sprayed after harvest, they enhance the strength of the next year's fruiting buds.

Spray with cowpat pit liquid or with liquid compost at a time approaching full moon during the growing season. Seaweed liquid manure is also useful (see Chapter 6).

Plate 1

Yarrow (*Achillea millefolium*)

Chamomile (*Matricaria chamomilla*)

Dandelion (*Taraxicum officinalis*)

European oak (*Quercus robur*)

Plate 2

Valerian (*Valerian officinalis*)

Stinging nettle (*Urtica dioica*)

Newly completed series of brick cowpat pits in south India.

Plate 3

Preparation 500.

Plants grown under different conditions: left, control; centre, using chemical fertilizers; right, in biodynamic soil.

Soil samples: left, original degraded soil; right, soil after two years of biodynamic farming.

Plate 4

Tree paste

The three ingredients of tree paste — clay, sand and cow manure — represent the three basic components of soil, which are united by the Preparation 500. Steiner spoke of the tree as being like soil raised up above the earth's surface; the bark is like the surface of the soil, and the twigs that grow each year are like annual plants growing out of the earth. Steiner also compared the cambium — the growing layer under the bark — to the roots which support these 'annual plants'. The tree paste nourishes and strengthens the 'bark/soil' and the cambium of the tree, to make it healthy.

Apply tree paste in the winter — after pruning but before bud-burst, and at a descending moon time — to stimulate tree growth and heal pruning cuts.

> **Tree paste**
> 1 part cow manure
> 1 part silica sand or diatomaceous earth
> 1 part potting clay or bentonite
> 2kg CPP per acre of trees

Mix these together with stirred Preparation 500 — sufficient to make a thin paste. For a small number of trees the paste can be painted on with a whitewash brush, as high as you can reach.

For a commercial orchard, the paste should be thin enough to be sprayed. Make it with bentonite and diatomaceous earth, rather than potting clay and silica sand, so it is easier to spray. Make sure the paste has been strained to remove any objects that could block the pump or nozzle. Also, choose a coarse nozzle and use a centrifugal rather than a diaphragm pump; the latter would be damaged by the nature of the materials.

The paste can be applied to all fruit trees and vines, but it should not be sprayed onto citrus trees, just applied around the base.

Disease control

If disease-resistant varieties have been planted it should be possible to avoid spraying fungicidal compounds on the trees. Other varieties can have one or two sprays of weak copper per year if necessary, when the trees are older. On already established orchards you will have to spray against pests and diseases at first. Copper sulphate, copper oxychloride or similar compounds are suitable fungicides.

In New Zealand the Demeter standards allow 1.2kg/acre per year of copper spray – this could be applied in three sprays of 400g/acre. The first spray should be before bud-burst. Spray copper or sulphur early before petal-fall against blackspot in apples and leafcurl in peaches. Later in the season spray 501 or equisetum just before a full moon, particularly at perigee, to protect trees against fungal diseases.

Application of liquid fertiliser such as seaweed or nettles strengthens the plants. However, you can't beat the blackspot on conventional apple varieties, unless it is a very dry spring. Feed the plants well-balanced compost. High concentrations of nitrogen cause 'blow-out' of fruit, making them more susceptible to fungus and pests.

Pheromone twist-ties can be used against codling moth. Building up a predator population on companion host plants also helps.

A tea made from well-made biodynamic compost with good bacterial and fungal qualities can be sprayed on apple trees fortnightly. The aim is that the tea, with its antagonistic bacteria and fungi, will compete with the harmful fungus or bacteria on the leaf of the tree. The tea will need to be aerated for one hour and should be put through a flowform or stirred for one hour.

See Chapter 6 for information on regular sprayings with CPP.

Subtropical fruit trees

Citrus, kiwifruit, avocados, persimmon, passionfruit, tamarillos and feijoas all need similar treatment.

Citrus

A citrus orchard is easy to convert to biodynamic management. Citrus trees are surface rooters and they like plenty of compost around their roots. Also apply compost over the whole area at the rate of 4–10 tonnes/acre. Compost for citrus should contain at least 10 per cent cow manure, as this will supply many of the trace elements needed for good citrus growth. Apply liquid fertiliser, especially seaweed, nettle and liquid cowpat pit, each month. Apply Preparation 500 four times a year. Preparation 501 is good for improving the taste of citrus. Apply it after flowering, when the fruit is just set, at a time when the moon and Saturn are in opposition, and just before harvest.

Disease control

The main disease problems of citrus are from melanose fungus, which causes spotted fruit, and verrucosis fungus (*Elsinoe fawcetti*), which causes corky growth on fruit and leaves, particularly in areas with high humidity, such as Northland, Bay of Plenty and South Auckland in New Zealand. A spray of weak copper at petal fall should control these diseases. Also, collect and burn all diseased fruit. Regular applications of the sequential spray to strengthen the plant, as described earlier, will go a long way toward combating all fungal diseases.

Uncomposted animal manures, particularly chicken manure, which has a high ammonia content, can cause very soft growth which encourages scale and aphids. The aphids exude honeydew on which black mildew grows, so that the fruit needs washing. So always use well-matured compost!

You need constant vigilance against borer, which can only be controlled manually. When harvesting, cut out any affected branch and burn it. You can kill borer by poking a piano wire down the borer hole.

Avocado

Avocados need a well-drained soil, as they are susceptible to Phytophthera (an indigenous soil fungus which attacks the roots of many exotic trees) when they get to about 11–12 years old. They also need plenty of compost to maintain a high fertility to support the surface-feeding roots. Avocado leaf mould contains a certain amount of phosphate, so encourage the build-up of leaf mould around the trees. Avocados may be infested by leafroller, but this is not generally a problem. Leafroller can be controlled by spraying with *Bacillus thuringensis* (BT).

To strengthen the plant also use the sequential spray as described earlier.

Persimmon

Persimmon also need plenty of compost. They tend to get mealybugs under the calyx. These can be reduced by pyrethrum or garlic sprays. Chilli pepper, garlic and ginger is an effective spray that is used in India against many insect pests.

Feijoa

Feijoas are easy to grow and do well in northern and eastern coastal areas of New Zealand. The fruit are difficult to market as they are watery, and have a short shelf-life. Feijoa trees tend to suffer from scale if too sheltered. The branches need

Feijoas in biodynamic home garden, Hawke's Bay.

to be thinned regularly and the last season's growth pruned. Give a good amount of compost and spray with Preparations 500 and 501 and reasonable applications of CCP manure.

Passionfruit

Passionfruit are normally grown from seed, and the plant usually lasts about three years. They need plenty of biodynamic compost, water and spraying with Preparation 500. Spraying 501 at the time when the moon is in opposition to Saturn will control most of the fungus.

Tamarillo

Tamarillos are quick-growing. They are much sweeter when grown biodynamically than conventionally; nitrogenous fertiliser makes them bitter. They are gross feeders, so use plenty of biodynamic compost — at least 10 tonnes per acre. Prune the plants after fruiting. Foliar feed once a month with biodynamic seaweed liquid manure.

Mildew on the leaves can be controlled by applying Preparation 501 at a time when the moon and Saturn are in opposition.

Preparation 501

Spray all subtropical fruit with Preparation 501 when the fruit is set, at a time when the moon and Saturn are in opposition, to improve fruit quality. Regular sprayings of 501 at this time will also strengthen the plants against mildew. To incorporate the 501 into your management system use the sequential spray as described.

Vineyards

For a new vineyard you may need to rip the soil before planting.

When planting the new vines incorporate well-matured compost into the planting holes. Dip the plants' roots into a slurry mixture of CPP to help root establishment.

Apply Preparation 500 plus CPP on the land twice in the autumn and twice again in the spring. This you can do every year.

During establishment of the new vineyard grow two successive green crops between the rows in spring and autumn to build up the humus. In spring sow oats, barley or buckwheat and vetch, and when grown in late summer disc in or use a spader to incorporate the green material into the soil. Then in the autumn sow tick beans or blue lupins together with either oats, rye corn or triticale. Then work into the soil in the spring.

Vineyard composting yard, Cromwell.

You may wish to repeat the above sequence of green crop. This will depend on the humus content of the soil.

In the following spring sow down a permanent sward or herbal ley between the vines. Depending on the soil and climate, such plants such as lucerne, red clover and cocksfoot can grow material which, when cut, can provide a useful mulch.

The aim with a vineyard is to encourage a deep rooting system, to increase and maintain good humus levels which will help to maintain good moisture levels without resorting to extensive irrigation systems.

This can be done by applying well-made biodynamic compost at planting time and with an annual maintenance dressing of compost at the rate of 5 tonnes per acre. It is best applied in the autumn after harvest, spreading the compost over the ground and not just around the stem of the grape. Remember the grape's roots extend throughout all the soil. Well-made, mature biodynamic compost will not increase the soluble nitrogen, which would lead to soft growth fungus and low-quality grapes. Also remember that well-made compost will encourage the presence of the mycorrhiza fungi whose very fine hyphae are part of the food web system that nourishes the grape.

In addition, use compost into which rock phosphate has been added to supply the phosphorus requirement (see compost making, Chapter 6).

Liquid manure made from seaweed will help the establishment and healthy growth of the vines, and can be used on a fortnightly basis. In addition, CPP can be used alternately with the seaweed. CPP can also be used as a spray on the vines after pruning.

Mulching with hay will conserve moisture and reduce irrigation. Make sure the hay has no hormonal spray residue; this would distort the growth of the vines.

Plant only vines that have been well grown. Check that the root stock of the vines have strong roots, an even, round stem, a healthy bud union and two strong buds of the scion. A weak plant will always be weak and will not be a good producer of grapes.

Commercial and home vegetable production

10

The successful production of a wide range of high-quality organically grown vegetables is probably the most satisfying achievement of any of the horticultural disciplines. It is also the most necessary and important, as vegetables play a large part in most people's diet. For this reason it is almost obligatory that vegetables for human consumption be grown to the highest quality without the use of chemical fertilisers or the possibility of residual pesticides.

Organic vegetable production is the most demanding of all crops, in terms of expertise and management skills, particularly to maintain a continuity of crop. It is hoped that the following guidelines will encourage more people to grow vegetables biodynamically.

Site selection

When starting out to grow vegetables, you can give yourself a great advantage if you choose a good block of land to suit the crops you will grow. Six things to consider are: aspect, soil type, climate, shelter, water supply and proximity to market.

Aspect

Choose land facing the morning sun: northeast in the southern hemisphere, and southeast in the northern hemisphere. This aspect will warm up more quickly in the spring, and will have less tendency to dry out than land which is subjected to the baking effect of the afternoon sun.

The land should be as level as possible: a slight slope to the northeast (to the southeast in the northern hemisphere) is an advantage for some crops, but make

A Hawke's Bay farm that has been managed biodynamically for thirty-five years.

sure you can use machinery easily. I have, however, seen a very successful market garden on quite a steep sunny hillside that had been terraced.

Make sure the land you buy is not wet and swampy or likely to flood.

Soil type

Look for fertile soil — it helps. A silty loam is the ideal. But check the soil's behaviour in climatic extremes; for example:

- How quickly does it dry out?
- What is it like when it becomes wet?
- Is it easy to cultivate?
- How deep is the topsoil?
- What is the drainage like?
- What is the underlying rock and is there a hard pan?
- What is the land's growing history?

Of course, the physical nature of the soil will be improved with the increase of the humus content through biodynamic management.

Climate

Climate is important in determining what crops can be grown and when. Aspects to look at are:

@ The distribution of rainfall.

@ Is the land frost-free, or how severe are the frosts?

@ How soon does the land warm up in spring?

@ How does the autumn temperature affect growth?

Local climatic conditions are possibly more important to consider:

@ Is the land in a frost pocket?

@ Is it exposed to the prevailing wind?

@ Is it in rain shadow (in an area that gets less rain than the normal district rainfall)?

Some areas and climates are especially suited to particular crops, for example in New Zealand Brussels sprouts grow well in South Canterbury, swedes in Southland and tomatoes and sweetcorn in Hawke's Bay.

Shelter

Good shelter can be a decided advantage for maximising the performance of the market garden land. Protection from the chilling effects of the southerly or the drying effects of a nor'wester can be provided by well-planted tree shelter. Much has been written on the subject of shelter; there is an excellent chapter on the subject in John and Bunny Mortimer's *Trees for the New Zealand Countryside* (1984). This chapter will point the market gardener to the many species available and the best position to plant them.

The lie of the land is also an important consideration. For instance, it is an advantage if the land slopes away from the prevailing cold or drying winds.

As shelterbelt planting I would recommend for New Zealand, alder (*Alnus rubra* or *A. glutinosa*) or *Casuarina cunninghamiana*, and New Zealand native plants — pittosporum (*Pittosporum eugenioides, tenuifolium* and *crassifolium*), kowhai (*Sophora microphylla*) or akeake (*Dodonea viscosa*), totara (*Podocarpus totara*) and taupata (*Coprosma repens*), to name a few suitable for salt winds. The Australian *Banksia integrafolia* is a wonderfully versatile tree. It grows from the coast to the centre of both islands in New Zealand. In other countries advice on suitable species should be sought from arborists.

Water supply

Check water supply, availability and quantity, and quality. Look particularly at the iron content in the water — iron is not conducive to making good liquid manures.

Proximity to markets

Travelling, transport and freight are very expensive in both time and resources. Positioning your farm close to the market means you, the grower, can have a good relationship with the consumer. This can also provide an important social aspect: customers can visit your farm and see how their vegetables are grown.

Soil fertility management

The maintenance and improvement of soil fertility in a market garden must be well thought through. A good management plan will ensure that the soil fertility will improve year by year.

The main consideration is the building up of the permanent humus in the soil. This can be done by:

- ◉ growing green manure (eg vetch and oats) between production crops
- ◉ using adequate amounts of compost
- ◉ adding liquid manures and the cowpat pit
- ◉ regular application of Preparation 500.

Crop rotation

A tool to maintain soil structure and humus is a well-planned crop rotation. It is a good idea to have sufficient land to return preferably half the land to growing soil-sustaining crops — either green crops or permanent pasture (for an example of a rotation, see Table 10.1). Putting land back into permanent pasture is the quickest way to increase its humus content. Also, with intelligent use of all the preparations, it is possible to maintain a fertile, healthy soil forever.

Ryecorn and tick beans as an autumn-sown green crop, Hawke's Bay.

Broadcasting ryecorn, oats and blue lupin as a green crop, Cromwell.

Green manuring

The wonderful thing about legumes in a strongly active biodynamic soil is that they can accumulate nitrogen out of the atmosphere at no cost. There are two main times for sowing green crops: autumn and spring.

Always sow a grain together with a legume, for example, in autumn use rye grain (ryecorn) or oats (black or white) together with either blue lupin, tick beans or hairy vetch.

Best results are obtained if you sow in early autumn, at a time when the moon and Saturn are in opposition. This crop would be turned into the soil just before the plant flowers.

If you sow in spring, use wheat, barley, oats or buckwheat together with blue lupins, broad beans, tick beans or vetch. Other species suitable for green manuring

Table 10.1: Suggested crop rotation for a market garden

Year		Plot 1	Plot 2	Plot 3	Plot 4
1	Autumn	WVC[1]	WGC[2]	PP[3]	PP
	Spring	SGC[4]	SVC[5]	PP	PP
2	Autumn	WVC	WGC	PP	PP
	Spring	SGC	SVC	PP	PP
3	Autumn	Sow PP	WGC	WVC	PP
	Spring	PP	Sow PP	SGC	SVC
4	Autumn	PP	PP	WVC	WGC
	Spring	PP	PP	SGC	SVC
5	Autumn	WVC	PP	Sow PP	WGC
	Spring	SGC	SVC	PP	Sow PP
6	Autumn	WVC	WGC	PP	PP

[1] WVC = Winter vegetable compost.

[2] WGC = Winter green crop — ryecorn or oats (black and white) together with blue lupin or tick beans or vetch.

[3] PP = Permanent pasture — Italian rye, cocksfoot, red clover, white clover.

[4] SGC = Summer green crop — oats, barley, wheat together with blue lupin or broad beans or tick beans, phacelia or mustard.

[5] SVC = Summer vegetable compost.

are mustard or phacelia (blue bee flower). Again, best results are obtained if you sow these in the period just before the moon and Saturn are in opposition in spring. Many combinations of species are possible, to give a wide variety that can be grown each season. This will allow a crop rotation within the green manuring programme.

A spring-sown crop would be ready to turn in about midsummer, before flowering and before the formation of seed. This is because at the time of seed formation the proteins in the leaf are being translocated to the seed; thus there would be less protein content in the crop to be converted into available nitrogen to feed the following production crop. On the other hand, if the green crop is left longer to mature, the higher carbonaceous material will add structure to the soil when turned in.

In turning the green crop in, it is best to use disc harrows to chop up the crop and incorporate it into the soil. The seedbed should be made with spring tyne cultivators. A rotary hoe is not a good tool to use because, although it turns in the green leafy crop satisfactorily, it can pulverise the soil and thus destroy its structure. It can also kill earthworms.

Compost application

The making of compost is described in Chapter 6.

Compost can be used in various stages of decomposition. When it is not fully broken down it will be higher in nitrogen and suitable for leafy crops. When well broken down it will be higher in carbon and more suitable for substance crops such as potatoes, kumara (sweet potato), sweetcorn, beans, squash etc. Remember that overuse of nitrogenous compost can cause plants to grow too rampantly and thus become susceptible to fungus and insect attack.

To feed the crop in a market garden, compost should be used at the rate of 20 cubic metres per acre.

Compost can be used in many ways. It can be broadcast in the spring over an area before growing a heavy-feeding field crop of potatoes, pumpkins or squash. It can be placed in furrows under crops such as brassicas, lettuce, tomatoes and various cucurbits for spring and autumn planting. Alternatively, it can be broadcast in autumn over the area that is going to be sown in green crop, which will encourage green manure growth and give a consequent increase in fertility derived from the turning in and breakdown of the crop. An area so treated would be suitable for salads and brassicas.

Application of liquid manures

Liquid manure is an effective plant tonic, particularly when it has been made using biodynamic Preparations 502–507. Liquids made from cow manure and cow urine, stinging nettle, seaweed and various weeds can be used at fortnightly intervals at the rate of 1:10, for example 4.5 litres of liquid manure to 45 litres of water per acre. (See Chapter 6 for instructions on preparing liquid manure.)

Spray the liquid towards evening when the dew is beginning to fall, just before full moon or around when the moon is in opposition to Saturn. It is a good idea to stir or put the mixture through a flowform for 10 minutes before applying.

How to use the cowpat pit

The cowpat pit has proved very effective when used as a liquid manure to bring health and vitality to the crops. It is a valuable way of bringing the influence of the Preparations 502–507 into the market garden.

Instructions on how to prepare a cowpat pit are given in Chapter 6. Use at the rate of 1kg in 40 litres of water per acre.

Application of Preparation 500

Apply Preparation 500 at least twice a year, in spring and autumn (preferably four times – twice in spring and twice in autumn) in a descending period of the moon (see Appendix 4, Understanding the planting calendar, and in New Zealand, the BioDynamic Association's *BioDynamic Farming and Gardening Calendar*). Apply in the afternoon at the rate of 25g (one portion) per acre (see Chapter 4 and Appendix 1).

It has been found over the years that this preparation improves soil quality in terms of structure, water-holding capacity and humus formation, encourages a deeper root penetration and strong, upright growth in plants, and brings an increase in earthworm activity.

Application of Preparation 501 (horn silica)

Usually Preparation 501 is applied when Preparation 500 is seen to be working, twelve months after first application. It is applied in spring and summer on an ascending period of the moon (see the *BioDynamic Farming and Gardening Calendar*). Apply early in the morning, just after sunrise, at the rate of 1g of 501 in 13 litres of warmed rainwater per acre (see Chapter 5).

Timing of application is important. The general rule is to apply Preparation 501 at an early stage in plant development, eg at the four-leaf stage, and again just before harvest. The effect of this is to enhance the photosynthesis process; it also seems to improve product quality, taste and shelf-life.

I have found over the years that spraying in the morning, just before the moon and Saturn are in opposition, will strengthen the plant against fungus and often against insect attack also (see Chapter 11, Calcium, silica and clay).

Preparations 502–507

These are incorporated into the composts, liquid manures and cowpat pit and applied.

Over the years I have found that the use of the preparations improves the fermentation processes in the breakdown of all biomass. The effect, as the preparations work through the composts, liquid manures and cowpat pit, is to improve the vegetables noticeably in terms of growth, quality, taste, freedom from pests and disease, and shelf-life.

Timing of operations

Market gardeners using biodynamic management will endeavour to become conversant with the rhythms of the moon. There are six rhythms that it is useful to know about:

1 the waxing and waning of the moon (new moon and full moon)

2 the time when the moon and Saturn are in opposition

3 ascending and descending

4 the perigee and apogee (the times when the moon is closest to and furthest from the earth respectively)

5 the node (the time when the moon's path and the sun's path coincide)

6 the rhythm of the moon's path through the constellations.

The opposition between the moon and Saturn is discussed in Chapter 11. See also Appendix 4, Understanding the planting calendar.

Using the available knowledge of these moon rhythms it is possible for the market gardener to choose an appropriate cosmic time to carry out any market-gardening operation.

Seed sowing

I have found, with thirty years' experience, that there is always a good germination at the time of full moon and also at the time of moon/Saturn opposition. However, plants germinated at the full moon are likely to be soft and leggy, whereas those germinated when the moon and Saturn are in opposition have more strength and structure, and are likely to develop into strong plants that can resist disease and pests.

Sowing seeds or cultivating the soil at appropriate times according to the moon's position in a particular constellation can enhance the inherent nature of the plant in question. For example, sowing or cultivating carrots when the moon is in Virgo, which is an earth constellation, definitely produces superior carrots; and sowing or cultivating lettuces when the moon is in a water constellation, eg Cancer or Scorpio, produces very good lettuces (see Thun, 1979, p 19).

Seed varieties

Use open pollinated seeds rather than hybrids, if you can obtain them, and choose known quality cultivars suitable for your district.

Avoid genetically engineered plants. The introduction of a gene into a plant to give it resistance to a certain insect or to a weedicide, for instance, is 'Band Aid' therapy. Dealing with insects or weeds in this way doesn't solve the root of the problem. Besides, what can be done when the insects become immune to that particular introduced insecticide gene? And what will that gene do to the person eating the food? Might it lead to future unexplained illnesses?

Transplanting seedlings

Transplant seedling vegetables when the moon is in a descending period. This particular fourteen-day period encourages very quick root development, since the growth energies are directed more towards the soil. This is probably one of the most useful rhythms for the market gardener when transplanting seedlings; provided plants receive adequate water, planting losses are dramatically reduced.

The occurrence of the node, which is approximately every 13.7 days, should always be noted as a time when no gardening operations should be carried out. The time from at least six hours before the node to three hours after should be avoided.

Disease and pest control

Remember that when the moon is approaching full or when it is close to the earth (the perigee) is a time when there is much moisture in the earth. This is when fungus can proliferate, so precautions should be taken – for example, using silica preparations such as 501 or 508 equisetum – to help to counteract the excess moisture.

Pests will also become rampant at full moon, so be aware of insect attacks, and take precautions.

Cultivation and weed control

Cultivation

Generally one wants to be as gentle as possible in the cultivation of the soil. Heavy tractors, deep ploughing and rotary hoeing are to be avoided.

When breaking in new land, disc up the pasture twice in autumn, allowing time for the turf to die off. Lightly plough to no deeper than 10cm, using a disc and harrow. If you avoid deep ploughing you will still be working within the living topsoil layer. Subsequent working-up of paddocks after a crop has been harvested can be done by chopping up the crop remains with discs, and making a seed or planting bed with the crumbler tiller. Any compost is spread before the discing. This is still working within the top 10cm of soil.

Incorporating a green crop

Run the disc over the green crop until it is worked into the soil. Leave it for three weeks, then work up the seedbed with a crumbler tiller.

Irrigation

You should not generally need to irrigate plants growing in soil that has been biodynamically managed and so has a reasonable humus content and good structure, as their roots penetrate deep into the soil. Remember that irrigating during a hot period will intensify the breakdown of the all-important humus, and will also bring the roots to the surface of the soil. Consequently the plants will then need more irrigation.

Much of the irrigation water used in the heat of the day will evaporate and be lost to the immediate water circulatory system. A general improvement of soil structure throughout the vegetable-growing areas of the world, by using biodynamic methods, would save the world millions of litres of water annually. This is particularly important where groundwater supplies are diminishing.

Weeding

Remember, one year's seeding means seven years' weeding.

If planting and sowing are done accurately, with the right spaces between rows, it is possible to set up a system whereby cultivators mounted on a tractor toolbar can effectively deal with weeds.

In a smaller market garden, manual wheeled hoes (eg Planet Junior) can be very effective. If you have a good labour force you can use hand hoes. It is beneficial to hoe early in the morning, when the dew can be incorporated into the soil.

Remember that the important thing is to hoe before you need to hoe. The job can be done twice as quickly before your crop is threatened with smothering weeds.

Another technique, of limited value, is pre-emergence flame weeding: a flame of butane is passed over the seedbed before germination to scorch off the newly germinated weed plants. In this way weeds can be eliminated, for example from a carrot or onion patch, before germination of the crop. However, use of this technique once the crop itself has germinated would be difficult.

One of the best methods of weed control is rotation; for example, regular growing of green crops and returning to pasture. Continual cultivations of one area will often lead to mineral deficiencies, and weeds will grow to try to correct these deficiencies.

An interesting weed-control method is to cultivate the soil lightly at the time when the moon is in the constellation of Leo. This constellation encourages the growth of all seedling plants – good and bad. As the weed seeds germinate, they can be lightly hoed off. This will eliminate the weeds in the top few centimetres of soil and give some relief from weeds for the next crop.

Another aspect to consider is that when you cultivate you bring in the influences of the cosmos. These cosmic influences enter the soil when it is disturbed. Therefore the cultivation of soil and plants at the right time will have great benefit.

Harvesting

Harvesting should always be done early in the morning to get maximum quality. Root crops should be harvested in a descending period, when the moon is in the constellation of Taurus (an earth constellation). If you are planning to store your vegetables, choose a time when the moon is in Gemini (an air/light constellation). Never harvest at full moon, as there is a high amount of moisture over the earth at that time, and vegetables such as pumpkins will be full of water and will not keep.

Home gardening

For the home gardener, cultivation times are the same, and the same conditions apply as for market gardening, except that they are scaled down. As the area is more limited it will not be possible to change your garden's situation, so more emphasis must be placed on compost-making, regular green cropping, and a comprehensive crop rotation system (see Table 10.2). Green manures play a very important part in the rotation, and in maintaining and improving the soil fertility. They prevent leaching of soil nutrients in the wet winter months, and stimulate

Tomatoes growing in a biodynamic greenhouse, Hohepa Poraiti, Hawke's Bay.

biological activity. In autumn, use ryecorn and vetch, oats and tick beans or blue lupins. In the summertime use barley and tick beans or similar plants.

In the home garden one of the best methods of crop rotation is to divide the production part of the garden into two parts: one is in crop while the other is growing a continuous green crop or maybe a grass mixture of Italian rye, chicory and clovers for two years. This can be mown regularly, leaving the clippings on the ground. This method will improve the soil structure.

The successful production of vegetables from the home garden plot requires, apart from good soil husbandry and the biodynamic compost, a knowledge of the varieties of plants and their correct sowing or planting time.

Table 10.3 gives sowing and planting times for a few popular vegetables, beginning with the spring garden. The timing is based on the central North Island climate — a temperate climate with moderate summer temperatures and cool winters, and 600–1500ml (25–60in) rainfall. I would suggest where possible, sow at a time when the moon and Saturn are in opposition.

Table 10.2: Suggested crop rotation for a home garden

	Year 1		Year 2		Year 3		Year 4
Bed	Autumn	Spring	Autumn	Spring	Autumn	Spring	Autumn
1	winter veg	roots	WGC[1]	beans & peas	WGC	cabbage salad	WGC
2	winter veg	SGC[2]	winter veg	roots	WGC	beans & peas	WGC
3	winter veg	SGC	winter veg	SGC	winter veg	roots	WGC
4	WGC	SGC	winter veg	SGC	winter veg	SGC	winter veg
5	WGC	cabbage salad	WGC	SGC	winter veg	SGC	winter veg
6	WGC	beans & peas	WGC	cabbage salad	WGC	SGC	winter veg

[1] WGC = Winter green crop: ryecorn or oats together with vetch, blue lupins, tick beans
[2] SGC = Summer green crop: barley, wheat, oats or buckwheat together with vetch, broad beans, French beans

Table 10.3: Home gardener's seed-sowing and planting guide for vegetable growing

Month	Sow		Plant	Harvest
July	Broccoli Fordhook		Aug/Sept	Nov/Dec
(under glass)	Cabbage Golden Acre		Aug/Sept	Nov/Dec
		Derby Day	Aug/Sept	Nov
	Cauli	All year round	Aug/Sept	Nov/Dec
		Four-Month Phenomenal	Aug/Sept	Nov/Dec
	Lettuce	Triumph	Aug/Sept	Nov
August	Broccoli Fordhook		Sept/Oct	Dec/Jan
(under glass)	Cabbage Golden Acre		Sept/Oct	Dec/Jan
		Derby Day	Sept/Oct	Dec/Jan
	Cauli	All year round	Sept/Oct	Dec/Jan
		Four-Month Phenomenal	Sept/Oct	Dec/Jan
	Lettuce	Great Lakes	Sept	Nov/Dec
		Buttercrunch	Sept	Nov/Dec
September				
(under glass)	Cabbage Succession		Nov	Jan/Feb
		Green Acre	Nov	Jan/Feb
	Lettuce	Great Lakes	Oct	Dec
		Buttercrunch	Oct	Dec
		Oak Leaf	Oct	Dec
	Tomato	Hardicross (dwarf)	Oct/Nov	Jan/Mar
		Moneymaker (tall) or		
		own choice	Oct/Nov	Jan/Mar
	Celery Utah		Nov	Feb/Mar
	Green Peppers Yoyo		Nov	Feb/Apr
(outdoors)	Leeks		Jan	Apr/Aug
	Onions	Pukekohe (long-keeper)		Dec/Feb
		California Red		Dec/Feb
	Carrot	Topweight		Dec
		Chantenay		Dec
		Manchester Table		Dec
	Parsnip Hollow Crown			May/Aug
	Spinach			Oct/Nov
	Silverbeet			Dec/Sept
	Red Beet			Nov/May
October				
(under glass)	Celery Utah		Jan	May/Aug
(outdoors)	Cabbage Savoy-type		Jan	May/Aug
	Brussels sprouts		Jan	May/Aug
	Curly kale		Jan	May/Aug

Continued

Month	Sow	Plant	Harvest
	Lettuce Great Lakes	Jan	Dec/Jan
	Buttercrunch		Dec/Jan
plus	Dwarf & climbing beans, pumpkin,		
	cucumber, melons, corn		Jan/Mar
	Carrot Topweight		Jan/Mar
	Chantenay		Jan/Mar
	Manchester Table		Jan/Mar
	Parsnip Hollow Crown		May/Aug
	Spinach		Nov/Dec
	Silverbeet		Dec/Sep
	Red Beet		Dec/Jan
November	Cabbage Savoy-type	Jan	Apr/Jul
(outdoors)	Curly kale	Jan	May/Jul
	Lettuce Great Lakes		Jan/Feb
	Buttercrunch		Jan/Feb
	Parsley		Jan/Jul
	Beans, corn, melons, courgettes,		Jan/Mar
	carrots, beetroot		Mar/Jul
December	Cabbage Winter Cross	Feb	May/Jun
(outdoors)	Cauli White Acre	Feb	May/Jun
	Broccoli Shogun	Feb	Apr/Jun
	Lettuce Great Lakes		Jan/Feb
	Buttercrunch		Jan/Feb
	Corn — last sowing		Mar
	Carrots		Apr/Jul
January	Cabbage Winter Cross	Mar	Jun/Aug
(outdoors)	Cauli White Acre	Mar	Jun/Aug
	Broccoli Shogun	Mar	Jun/Aug
	Lettuce Great Lakes		Feb/Mar
	Buttercrunch		Feb/Mar
	Mignonette	Mar	Apr/May
	Cos	Mar	Apr/May
February	Cabbage Winter Cross	end Mar	Jul/Sept
(outdoors)	Cauli White Acre	end Mar	Jul/Sept
	Broccoli Shogun	end Mar	Jul/Sept
	Lettuce Mignonette	end Mar	Apr/May
	Cos	end Mar	Apr/May
	Spinach		Apr/May
March	Spinach		Apr/May
April	Broad beans		Sept/Oct
	Spinach		Jun/Jul

Home garden compost

Making and tending your compost heap should be high on the list of autumn and winter jobs: either turning your existing heap or using all the materials you have gathered to make a new one. Your heap should be piled together loosely, keeping everything moist, and mixing the animal manure with the other organic materials from your clean-up. Remember your heap should get quite hot. You can make your heap either in a compost bin or using the windrow system (see notes on compost-making in Chapter 6).

Materials particularly suited for home garden composts are:

- kitchen scraps

- lawn clippings

- chopped or mulched prunings (eg hedges, fruit trees, roses)

- blood and bone

- rock phosphate.

Bin-type compost can be built up gradually as material becomes available. Make in batches weekly or fortnightly to encourage the heat process. Cover with damp jute sacks or old carpet during building. You will need two bins — one for the finished compost and one for the compost in the process of being made — and an area for the storage of new compost materials.

Add biodynamic compost preparations when the heap or batch is finished being built. Compost is ready when it breaks down easily between finger and thumb and can be moulded into a shape. In most cases, a barrowload spread over 6 square metres is sufficient.

Calcium, silica and clay

Rudolf Steiner gives a clue as to the importance of calcium and silica in his Agricultural Lectures. He points out frequently that an important aim in biodynamic agriculture is to bring about a balance between the calcium and the silica and that the clay mediates between the two.

Characteristics

Generally calcium, or limestone as it is commonly known, is beneficial for the successful growing of many crops, although it is not known exactly why. An overuse of limestone rock can oxidise organic matter or the humus with a temporary increase of fertility but with the loss of humus which will lead eventually to soil degradation.

In nature, pure calcium carbonate has a tendency to make varied forms which we see in the wide variety of the seashells. Other examples are seen in stalactites and stalagmites and in the bones of mammals and fish.

Conventional science says very little about silica except that it occurs generally on the skin or the bark of most living things. Some of these plants have very tough, thorny bark and spiny leaves — gorse, for example, and some of the hard thistles. An unusual plant is the equisetum or horsetail, which contains much silica in a living form. Equisetum does not appear to have silica so much on the surface of the leaf, but when the leaves are burnt they leave a skeleton or framework of silica in the ashes. The casuarina, or Australian sheoak, will do the same thing.

In nature, silica occurs in hard rocks and various compound minerals, and in its purest form as silicon oxide, where we see it as a clear quartz crystal.

The calcium structure which shows itself in the forms of shells and bones is relatively soft and less permanent than the hard crystal of quartz. Seashells or eggshells will break very easily, whereas quartz needs to be broken up with strong blows of a hammer. Perhaps the form and the substance expressed in these two minerals show how the processes work in nature.

Steiner says that the calcium force in the earth comes from the planets closer to the sun — the moon, Mercury and Venus; while those planets further out than the earth from the sun — Mars, Jupiter and Saturn — bring in the silica influences.

Processes

A natural process could be described as what brings about anything you see in nature. We don't actually see the process working, but we see the final result, whether it is a crystal, a plant, an animal or a human being. These processes are still not well understood, and various theories have been advanced to try to explain what happens.

For example, look at the shell formation of an egg. In 1972 a French scientist, Louis Kevran, suggested that the calcium content of a chicken egg was directly connected not to the calcium in the hen's diet, but rather to the hen's ability to combine potassium and hydrogen in its food to form the calcium needed for the shell (see Harold Willis, *The Coming Revolution in Agriculture*, pp 181, 182). This calcium-forming activity can be described as a calcium process.

The shell formation of molluscs is a similar process. Sea water does not appear to contain sufficient calcium for the shell: its formation is dependent on a calcium process from the cosmos, working through the water.

Steiner pointed out that the limestone processes are connected to the form of plants, the shape of their leaves, fruit etc, and importantly, their seeding and reproduction.

Where limestone is present in the soil, earthworm activity increases; there is a limestone process within the gut of the earthworm. The nodulation on all legume roots also increases in the presence of limestone, as do the various soil bacteria.

The silica processes, in contrast, are connected to the building up of the substance of the plant, namely the part we eat. They are there to help the building up of starches, sugars and proteins in the plant.

Bearing all the above in mind, how do we go about enhancing the balance between the calcium and the silica on a farm under biodynamic management?

Practical considerations

Preparation 500 is made from dung from a lactating cow, which will have many of the processes of calcium coursing through its metabolic system. It is reasonable to suppose that those calcium energies will be contained in the dung. So when we spray our land with 500 we are bringing the calcium processes into the soil. This is borne out by on-farm observations of the increases in earthworm activity and legume nodulation as mentioned above, and the increase in humus with resultant improvements in soil structure.

The use of Preparation 501 (horn silica) is an obvious way of bringing the silica processes onto the farm. When 501 is used where the 500 has already been working, there is a noticeable improvement in plant health and nutritional quality, and in stock health. The use of these two sprays containing the inherent qualities of these two minerals works towards the balancing of their activity in the soil.

If we consider the planetary influences, we can see that these can be used as well to reinforce the calcium–silica processes. When studying a planting calendar we can observe various planetary connections. One of these is the opposition of the moon and Saturn — that is, when these two planets are on opposite sides of the earth. The moon, being closer to the sun, brings in calcium processes (form), and Saturn, being furthest away from the sun, brings the silica processes (substance). Now, if seeds are sown at the time when the moon and Saturn are in opposition, the plant gathers the balance from these two influences into itself, bringing great strength and quality to the resulting growth of the plant. I have observed this effect time after time over the past twenty-eight years.

So to complement the use of Preparation 500 we spray the silica Preparation 501 on the plants. Preparation 501 brings to the plant very much what is happening in the constellations, so when it is sprayed at the time of moon/Saturn opposition, again the balancing of the calcium and limestone takes place.

Just one more observation to think about: Preparation 505 made from oak bark is high in lime, and Preparation 506 made from dandelion is strong in silica processes. Here is another possibility to bring about this balance when using compost and cowpat pit or liquid manures.

Clay in relation to calcium and silica

Rudolf Steiner makes several references to clay, in relation to silica and calcium, in his Agriculture course. On page 31 of *Agriculture* he states, 'What is collected down below from the cosmos (via the silica) must always be able to stream upward, and the presence of clay in the soil makes this possible. Substances like clay support the upward flow of the effects of the cosmic entities in the ground.' Again on page 31, 'All the forces and fine homoeopathic substances produced by means of water and air above the ground are drawn down by the soil's greater or lesser content of lime. It is the lime in the soil and the presence of calcareous substances in homoeopathic doses just above the soil's surface that serve to draw this terrestrial factor into the ground.' On page 33 he says, 'if we are dealing with a soil that does not carry these influences upward during the winter as it should, it is good to furnish the soil with some clay, the dosage of which I will indicate later.' (To my knowledge Steiner never did give the indications of the amount of clay.) And further on page 60 he says, 'and clay mediates between them (silica and limestone). Clay is closer to silica but it still mediates towards lime.'

These comments suggest that in working with biodynamic agriculture we should somehow include clay into our management system. Clays are formed from various rocks containing aluminium silicates that are well weathered. Such materials as feldspar, bentonite or basalt are well known and can be used.

Clay is used as one of the ingredients in the tree paste, which incidentally is made from sand or diatomaceous earth (silica), cow dung (calcium) and clay or bentonite (clay) (see p 97). Basalt dust is used in the making of the cowpat pit (see p 59). Any of these rock dusts can be sprinkled through the compost heap.

I have made the horn clay using local bentonite, buried in a cowhorn over the winter in a separate pit from the cow manure 500. I stirred it and spread it in the same way as the 500, using 10g in 13.5 litres. I use it in the afternoon following the 500 spray. I have also used it as part of the sequential spray where all the biodynamic preparations are used – 500 and CPP on the first morning, 501 the following morning, clay that afternoon, and equisetum the following morning. I have seen some very good results from this sequence with regards growth and strength of the plants (see p 51).

There are questions – for instance, do we bury the clay also over the summer? At the same time as 501 but not in the same hole, and then spray in the morning? Try it and see what results you get.

Early work in Europe making Preparations 500 and 501 included putting a plug of clay in the end of each horn before burying. This does make sense in light of Rudolf Steiner's comments regarding the importance of clay.

A guide to practical observations | 12

As soon as I walk onto a farm I can tell if it is being farmed properly according to biodynamic principles. On a biodynamic farm, there is a sense of life, of health, of balance. There is a particular smell — of the cows' breath, of the dung. Other biodynamic farmers have observed this as well. Walk into a cowshed during milking: on a biodynamic farm you will notice settled, quiet cows, pleasant-smelling dung, sweet-smelling milk in the vat, and an unstressed farmer happy in his or her job. Good powers of observation are of great importance in animal and crop husbandry.

Assessment of pasture and crop quality

A good-quality pasture on good soil will recover quickly after drought. But you don't have to wait for a drought to assess your pasture quality. At any time you can read what the pasture is telling you. It should have an upright nature — particularly the clovers — and have a firm look and a healthy green colour.

In pastures that are more than 10–12cm long, the grass and clover stems should be green with chlorophyll right down to the base. If soluble fertilisers have been put on the pasture, the base of the stems will be white.

To test the grass quality, see how easily you can pull a blade apart. You can learn to gauge the tensile strength of plants. Grass with low tensile strength is low in fibre, and cows need a good fibre content. If the grass feels soft, it has been over-manured.

You can also chew the grass to assess its fibre content, and to see if it tastes sweet or bitter. Exercise some caution with this test — there may be worm eggs on the grass, particularly on a badly managed farm.

You can learn to distinguish from the taste of brassicas whether a plant is sweet or whether it has the bitterness associated with overuse of nitrogen during growth. Brassicas are good indicators of the extent of biodynamic activity in the soil, and the extent to which the nitrogen has been mineralised. Unmineralised nitrogen taken up in the nitrite form will make the brassicas taste bitter.

Assessing when to cut hay is important. It should be done on a light/air day to ensure better leaf preservation. Hay and silage that has been sprayed with Preparation 501 prior to cutting has a unique fragrance — you can smell that 501 has been used.

All biodynamic farmers should cultivate their sense of smell, in order to recognise many biodynamic processes. The skills developed will serve as well as any laboratory. I remember the time when Dr Herbert Koepf visited New Zealand. I took him for a walk in the bush between Tauranga and Rotorua. Herbert picked a fern frond that was decomposing and smelled it. 'Ah, *Bactidiomyces*,' he exclaimed. If you keep practising, you will be able to smell the presence of bacteria, fungi and other things.

The sense of smell can also be used to assess the quality of milk, vegetables or sheep dung. I can tell by smelling some compost whether it has had biodynamic compost preparations added to it or not. You can check the quality of the 500, liquid manure and cowpat pit by smelling them.

Animal characteristics

A good understanding of the basic characteristics of each animal type assists in the understanding of their place on the farm and the conditions they need. Observe a cow lying down chewing her cud. See how she seems to belong near the earth; she almost sinks into it, and gets up with difficulty. Compare her with birds flying — they seem to be ruled by levity; the cow by gravity. The cow relates strongly to the earth, whereas sheep are less settled — they are orientated more towards the light. Horses are different again — like the wind. These characteristics affect the character of the manure which each animal produces.

A cow complements the look of a paddock — she belongs there, in a way that sheep, goats and deer do not. Sheep and goats belong on the hills, where there are shrubs to browse. When sheep are kept in meadows they tend to have health problems such as footrot, scouring and worms, and they grow too fat. Horses belong on the plains. Pigs belong in forests, where they root and forage. If you take an animal away from its natural environment it will tend to become ill. For further discussion of animal characteristics, see Steiner's *Man as Symphony of the Creative Word*; also Koenig, *Man and the Domestic Animal*.

It is interesting to watch what plant species cows eat when you put them into a new paddock. Such observations are useful when deciding what species you should sow.

Your senses can be sharpened to observe all kinds of natural events which you may not have noticed before, and which help you to understand more about plants and animals and how they grow. Have you ever noticed that at sunrise and at sunset the air seems to get colder? At those times there is movement of water and air in and out of the earth. This movement brings the cooling effect.

You will find that your sense of smell and observational skills will improve over the years just as your farm will improve over time. The results of biodynamic management are impressive, but don't expect them to be instant.

Biodynamic farming on the move — some practical examples

13

Nowhere in the world is farming an easy task, be it growing apples, mangoes, corn, rice, vegetables, sheep, goats or cows. It will always be a task that demands the expertise of the farmer who, with skilful management of the farm and use of biodynamic techniques, makes a success of growing the crop. There is a tremendous joy in the growing of such a crop and in knowing that the people who eat it will be well nourished, and that this has been done without harming the environment.

The application of sound biodynamic methods will very much increase the success of the crop being grown; in fact, as the years of using the biodynamic preparations roll by, the successes far outweigh the disappointments.

I have noticed throughout the world at biodynamic gatherings there is a cheerfulness and positivity that one does not experience at other gatherings of farmers. Biodynamic farmers will always share their knowledge and new ideas about this way of agriculture, and this creates a sense of community and the quiet feeling that things are going well down on the farm.

And there are many stories about things going well on the farm and in the orchard. What follows is an account of some farms that have either full Demeter or trans-Demeter certification. In each case the farmers and orchardists are experienced and good operators.

Note: in all the following examples, phosphate in the form of rock phosphate and agricultural limestone is applied only where it is perceived that the land needs it. This can be determined by observing pasture growth. Lack of clovers and a predominance of flat weeds will indicate a need for phosphate or lime. Have your soil checked by a soil laboratory.

Dairy farm

A dairy farm which has been under biodynamic management for ten years in the north of New Zealand is running 200 cows on 200 acres.

There is a regular application of Preparation 500 twice a year along with seaweed liquid manure made with Preparations 502–507. The 500 is mixed using a Jaerna model Virbela flowform and is applied by tractor with a 450-litre spray rig.

The cowshed effluent is run through the flowforms with Preparations 502–507 being added in the form of the cowpat pit before it is spread over the pasture with a travelling irrigator (see Chapter 7).

There is good pasture growth during most of the year with mixed herbage and strong clover growth. Adequate conservation of silage and hay is made each year. The soil structure is well formed, with roots penetrating deep into the soil, good clover nodulation and an active earthworm population. The stock are all healthy and there is little call for the services of the vet. Animal deaths on this farm are 1–2 per cent. It is interesting that stock health is noticeably better than on neighbouring farms using conventional farming methods. Overall production of milk is on a par with the district average, and because of the lower inputs – no fertilisers, less spent on animal health and cow replacements for a variety of reasons – this farm is economically sound.

Sheep and beef farm #1

This farm is on the east coast of the North Island of New Zealand. It is 1800 acres of hilly to rolling country and runs 2000 ewes and 300 cattle of mixed ages. The preparations have been applied for ten years.

Preparation 500 is applied twice a year, along with liquid seaweed, in the spring and autumn. Because of the large area of this farm the only practical way to apply the preparations and liquid manures is by helicopter. The 500 is mixed in the large capacity flowform VB500, which can mix 2500 litres easily in one hour. This amount of liquid is sufficient to keep the aircraft operating. Because of the size of this farm the amount of water and Preparation 500 used per acre has been reduced to half of what is normally used: 25g of 500 in 13 litres of water is spread over 2 acres instead of one. This rate is not recommended for small farms.

The effectiveness of this method of application is borne out by the obvious results in soil quality and animal health. The soil is of very good structure showing the typical nutty, crumbly particles. The grass roots are deep and the farm does not dry out to the extent that other farms in the district do. Earthworm activity is very good with all the cowpats being incorporated into the soil in a short time.

The cattle look brilliant and are in good health and shining, with little or no use of drenches. Only the lambs are drenched, with herbal drenches of garlic and cider vinegar. There is no fly-strike on sheep on this farm (this is a terrible problem on most farms in this part of the world). I am sure this is because the good-quality pasture results in good-quality dung which does not attract the blowfly in the same way as chemically fertilised pasture does. Also, the animals are more healthy and do not attract many flies.

Sheep and beef farm #2

This farm is a smaller unit of 300 acres in central Hawke's Bay on the east coast of the North Island of New Zealand. It is on moderately hilly to rolling country with a heavy clay loam soil. The farm carries 11.6 stock units per hectare.

The farm has been under biodynamic management for twelve years. Preparation 500 has been applied regularly twice a year, along with the applications of liquid fish manure and liquid seaweed.

The heavy nature of the soil has changed noticeably over this time when compared with the conventionally managed farm next door. The roots go much deeper into the soil, and there is a wonderful mixing of the subsoil and the topsoil by the earthworms at a depth of 30cm (12in) or more, which has increased the living topsoil layer. There is good clover nodulation.

The pasture where the land has been flat enough to work up and resow in herbal ley is very good. One paddock of chicory and red clover is exceptional in terms of the bulk and quality of fodder grown. The rest of the farm on the hilly parts is growing mostly rye, white clover and native grasses, which are also an indication of the quality one expects from soils where the preparations are used. It is interesting to note that in all pastoral farms under biodynamic management, farmers report that stock appear to be satisfied with less fodder while still making the same weight gain or making milk. It has been shown (MacGregor, pers. comm. 1996) that biodynamically grown grass has a greater dry-matter content than chemically grown grass.

Stock health is good and successful use is made of herbal drenches for young stock.

Because this farm is quite small by New Zealand standards, to support a family the decision was made to add value to its products. Using the market advantage of the Demeter certification, they sell the lamb and beef locally at a premium. The Romney wool is spun into yarn and handknitted into jerseys and baby clothes, and machine knitted into socks, hats and gloves. This wool is soft and knits up beautifully.

Mixed cropping farm

This farm is in north Canterbury in the South Island of New Zealand. It is 400 acres of flat alluvial soil and a block of 400 acres of hill country which is not all Demeter. On the flats there are 100 acres under crops; wheat, oats, rye, and barley as well as lentils. The farm runs 1000 stock units of cattle and 1000 stock units of sheep over both areas.

The pastures are mostly mixed herbal, having been resown at the end of the rotation of the cropping. The cattle play a very important part in the maintenance of the fertility of the land. They are overwintered on a pad, and the dung and litter is composted and put back onto the paddock.

Preparation 500 is applied twice a year in late spring and early autumn over the flat 400 acres and on the flat and rolling areas of the hills. Cowpat pit manure made with Preparations 502–507 is applied over the farm regularly. Preparation 501 is applied to the grain and lentil crops at the beginning of the growth and just before harvesting. The preparations are applied with tractor and spray rig.

Animal and plant health is good.

The main thrust of this operation is the supplying of processed farm produce to the people who want to eat Demeter-quality food. The wheat, barley and rye are milled into flour on the farm and the oats are rolled. Fat lambs and beef are sold as certified organic produce on the local market.

Market garden

This property is 10 acres in South Canterbury and has been under biodynamic management for fifteen years. At any one time there would be approximately 5 acres under crop or green manure; the remainder would be in pasture and have cattle grazing on it. Two or three cows are kept on an overnight pad and the manure is collected each morning for compost-making. Herbs and vegetables are grown; the vegetables are those which are suitable for the district, which is well known for its Brussels sprouts, carrots, onions, and potatoes.

Compost is made regularly using the cow manure from the yard, crop wastes, and hay cut from the property. The compost preparations are added to the compost pile when the heap is completed. The compost-making in this garden has developed over the years to a very high standard. Compost is applied at the rate of 20 tonnes per acre to brassica and potato crops; onions and carrots get less (about 10 tonnes per acre). Seaweed liquid manure made with Preparations 502–507 is applied at least once a month as a tonic.

This market garden pays great attention to using the cosmic rhythms in all its gardening operations, with great success.

Preparation 500 is applied twice a year — in spring when the soil has warmed up (during the descending period of the moon and in the afternoon), and again in early autumn at the descending period of the moon. Preparation 501 is sprayed on the crops in the early morning close to harvest time when Saturn is in opposition to the moon. The seeds are sown generally at the moon/Saturn opposition, making use of the information in the BioDynamic Association's *BioDynamic Farming and Gardening Calendar* (see Appendix 4, Understanding the planting calendar). Harvesting is done at the appropriate time according to the calendar.

The produce from this market garden is of very high quality and the taste is superb. It is sold as Demeter produce in the South Island.

A final note about the soil: it is improving year by year even though it is being cropped. With careful attention to composting, green manuring, crop rotations, sensitive cultivation, regularly returning the land back to pasture, and applying Preparation 500, the soil humus and the depth of the soil are increasing.

Citrus orchard

This citrus orchard is in the Northland region of New Zealand, growing oranges and tamarillos. It is 10 acres, fully planted with plenty of space between rows. It has been biodynamically managed for ten years.

Preparation 500 is used twice a year. Compost and seaweed liquid manure made with Preparations 502–507 are used once a month. A very good sward of white clover and kikuyu grass has been developed, which grows very vigorously and is mown regularly; the mowings provide a wonderful mulch. The weeds around the trees are dealt with by hand once or twice a year.

It is interesting to note that the growth and vigour of the sward goes beyond the boundary of the orchard over into the neighbour's orchard for 30 metres or more, until it gradually stops. This is a phenomenon that is repeated in most places where Preparation 500 is used – the neighbouring land alongside the boundary shows the soil improvement typically associated with the use of this preparation.

The fruit is of very high quality, sweet, keeps well, and sells well.

Avocado-growing

This is not an observation of a specific orchard, but after visiting several bio-dynamic orchards I have come up with the following.

Avocados grow quite well in the warmer places of New Zealand where it is frostfree and there is good soil drainage. They are very easy to grow under biodynamic management and the use of the full range of preparations makes for good-tasting fruit. Leaf mould builds up under the canopy of the bigger trees, into which the feeding roots will run. This will happen only where no chemical weed sprays have been used under the trees.

Compost application is very important, as avocados are gross feeders. It should be applied liberally under and up to the dripline. Liquid seaweed manure should be sprayed regularly, at least once a month. As the trees reach large proportions a special spray rig will be needed for this task.

There are, however, a few problems that occur in avocado growing. After about ten to twelve years all the trees of this age throughout the growing areas, biodynamic or conventional, die back. There are several theories as to why. One suggested cause is the root fungus phytophthera. When the tree begins to age and the roots become less vigorous, they are killed by the fungus. This is, I think, a secondary problem due to lack of vigour.

Another theory is that only the variety Hass is affected; all other varieties seem to be able to cope. Unfortunately, Hass is the most popular variety grown.

Yet another theory is that, because the trees have been planted so close, there has been a heavy demand on nutrition and no nutrients are left in the soil to support growth. The trees become less vigorous, and the roots are then attacked by the phytophthera root fungus as previously mentioned.

This last theory seems the most likely: I have seen health return to trees when the tree is cut back to stimulate new growth, and masses of compost and mulch is put around the dripline to encourage the young feeding roots that reappear.

In another instance, a very heavy dressing of seaweed meal was worked into the soil around the dripline of one of a group of trees that had lost most of their leaves. With this boost of fertiliser, the leaves came back, while the other trees that were not treated with any seaweed did not recover.

Obviously this die-back problem is a classic case of a monoculture gone wrong. To grow the avocado biodynamically one should first look for natural companion plants. Plant a mixed subtropical orchard and maintain the fertility of the land right from the beginning with composts and mulches, and use all the preparations in the ways mentioned in this book to maintain and sustain soil fertility.

Pharmaceutical herb growing in Havelock North

Herbs for Weleda are being grown in this 5-hectare garden in Hawke's Bay, New Zealand. The garden is attractively laid out and well maintained, with older trees and some more recently planted trees featuring on the boundaries.

It has been intensively managed biodynamically for the past six years. Herbs are grown for processing into pharmaceutical products. Such herbs as thyme, yarrow and the narrow-leafed plantain are grown and the leaf is dried. Dried flowers grown include calendula, lavender, field poppy, viola and yarrow. Fresh

Inula and echinacea growing in the Demeter herb garden, Havelock North.

flowers include calendula, chamomile, echinacea, hypericum, primula, rue, onopordum and valerian. And then there are the roots such as archangelica, celedonium, inula, valerian and echinacea, which are harvested in winter.

During the manufacturing processes in the factory the fragrance of the herbs wafting through the building is wonderful. And of course the essentials oils are so much more pungent with the herbs that have been grown biodynamically, particularly where 501 has been used.

Maintaining soil fertility is the aim of the overall management. This is done with regular green manuring and compost-making as well as horn dung 500 application.

Green manures are mostly grown as a winter crop with tick beans or blue lupin with either oats or ryecorn sown in autumn. This will be disced into the soil in time for the spring sowing and planting.

Compost-making plays a big part in this management, and very well-matured compost that has gone more towards the formation of permanent humus is used. This encourages quality herbal growth. Fresh, immature compost will make a soft leafy growth.

The gardens have a small dung herd of four cows, which provides dung for the

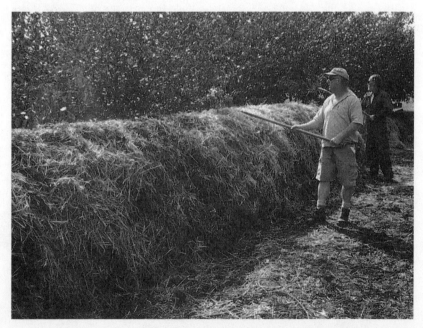

Compost at the Demeter herb garden, under the shade of an alder hedge.

compost making. They are kept overnight on a straw pad which facilitates collection of the dung and urine. The compost is made by collecting up all this bedding, which is mixed with ensiled grass and any herbal wastes from production. The heap is built in the shade, under a row of alder trees, and the compost preparations are always used in the compost. About 60 cubic metres of compost are made annually.

Preparation 500 is made at the gardens and used at least twice a year, in spring and autumn. It is stirred in a wooden barrel using a suspended rod.

Cowpat pit manure is always being made on a small scale and is used regularly.

I think what is nice about this garden is the atmosphere one experiences when one is walking through it. It is the same in most biodynamic gardens or farms, difficult to explain but something to do with being very aware of and being connected to the growth taking place — the smell of the earth, the softness of the soil, and the earthworm activity. I think it is our connection with the elemental beings that Rudolf Steiner talks about, and I think this connection comes through the regular use of the biodynamic preparations in the garden. This must be a wonderful thing for the growing of herbs that are used for making medicines to heal people.

Germinating ryecorn and tick beans, an autumn-sown green crop, Hawke's Bay.

Hohepa Poraiti

In the hills west of Napier, in Hawke's Bay, there is a Demeter-certified vegetable garden which has been using the biodynamic preparations since 1974.

It is approximately 10 hectares, about half of which is under cultivation at any one time. Vegetables and fruits are grown to supply the Hohepa communities in Hawke's Bay (residential homes and schools where work opportunities are given to people in need of special care, based on the Steiner model). Because of the garden's relatively sheltered position it is possible to grow vegetables very well all the year.

The main crops grown are kumara, leeks, celery, carrots, pumpkin, squash and greens. Early tomatoes are grown in a large glasshouse. The taste of all these vegetables is wonderful, and they receive very favourable comments from those who eat them. Surplus vegetables are sold on the open market.

There is compost being made all the time from cow dung, straw, a variety of crop wastes, and kitchen scraps from the residential houses. The composts are made by hand, and this is a great activity for the Hohepa resident gardeners. There is much hand work done here apart from compost making, such as sowing and planting, and the continuous hoeing and weeding.

Very good quality vegetable seedlings are grown in a glasshouse — lettuces, cabbages, cauliflowers and celery and kumara. They are grown in very well-matured compost that has been sieved.

For a number of years all the preparations for the New Zealand BioDynamic Association have been made at Poraiti. The dung for the 500 is collected from the Hohepa Clive dairy farm. All the herbs are grown during the year in the gardens, from where they are picked, dried and stored.

Often the preparation-making time provides the opportunity to teach other biodynamic practitioners the art of making the preparations.

The end of the chain — organic food retail outlets

In 2004 there are definitely more organically grown food products available for the public to buy, and the demand from the discerning consumer is increasing.

Along with many cities and towns throughout the world, in New Zealand numbers of what are called 'health food' shops are springing up. There is one such shop in Hastings city, in Hawke's Bay — a small but very attractive and well-run

Health food shop, Hastings.

food shop where there is an excellence of presentation. This shop is well stocked with a very wide range of consumer goods, such as vegetables, fruits and nuts, various grains and flours, pulses, dairy products such as milk, yoghurt, quark and cheeses, and also free-range eggs, jams, honey and oils, biscuits and breads. There is also tea, coffee and a wide range of spices, and there are health care products.

The owners prefer to source as much of their stock as possible from biodynamic growers, and in particular those with the Demeter certification trademark. They and their customers can recognise the difference in quality, taste and nutritional value in food grown this way. The food is all labelled with its organic status.

Here are a few comments from customers of the shop when asked why they shop there:

'It is in a good location and I have a preference for organic produce. There will be no GE here.'

'Organic produce means that the production of crops is better for the earth. It is a safe place to shop as there are no chemicals on the food.'

'I like what they sell. There is a good smell in this shop and it is very attractive.'

'I want good organic food, I like the flavour and I know it is safe to eat.'

'I have a preference for organic food. It is healthier for you and it tastes better.'

'There is a big range of food here and it is of consistent good quality.'

Grape-growing for raisin production

This vineyard is in Fresno, California, near the foothills of the Sierra Mountains. The main crops grown in this district are almonds and grapes. The vineyard covers 50 acres and is surrounded by conventional growers. The soil is very light and of a sandy nature, washed down from the granite mountains. There is very little humus. The area is flood-irrigated once a month. The variety of grapes grown is Thompson's Seedless. The climate is mild, ranging from a slight winter chill to extremely hot summer temperatures, which makes for good raisin production.

This vineyard has been biodynamic for four years. Preparation 500 has been applied twice a year and sometimes more often, with monthly sprayings of Preparation 501 during the growing season. A stirring machine is used, and a tractor spray rig for application.

Compost is applied over half the orchard each year. The compost is made from brought-in cow manure and straw or old hay and goes through a hot fermentation process with Preparations 502–507 added. Seaweed manure is applied during the growing season. A green manure crop of oats, blue lupin and vetch is grown after harvest in alternate rows and disced in before bud break. Weeding is done by cultivation.

The vineyard is showing some very noticeable differences from the neighbouring vineyards which are chemically fertilised, chemically weeded and chemically sprayed for pests and diseases. The soil structure is very much improved. The growth of cane for next year's crops is strong, and internodes are close but well spaced for a good crop compared with the neighbouring vineyard where the nitrogen-boosted plants have widely spaced internodes. The good cane growth is due to the 501 sprayings, and there is a very low incidence of insect attack on leaves. Production is better than average, and most importantly, the superior taste of the raisins is widely acclaimed.

Mango-growing

These orchards are in the south of India in the district of Madurai, in the foothills of the Palni Hills near Kodaikanal.

There are several orchards with a total of 1500 acres being managed biodynamically for the past two years, although the first orchard of 150 acres was converted four years ago. It was the success of the management of this orchard that inspired other growers to do the same.

This orchard dehydrates all its fruit in a solar-heated factory on one of the farms. Other fruits such as bananas, pineapples and pears are also dried and are sold on the German market.

Preparation 500 is sprayed at least twice a year and 501 at least once. These preparations are all stirred by hand. The 500 is also applied by hand with a brush but the 501 is sprayed in a mist above the trees using a pump and a nozzle on the end of a long wand.

There has been a tremendous amount of compost made from crop wastes, factory wastes from the dehydrating plant, cow-dung slurry, reservoir tank silt, and coconut fibre. The compost is applied regularly around the dripline of the trees, and liquid manure sprays are made from neem leaves, cow manure, cow urine, and from the foliage of various legume trees. The cowpat pit is applied over all the orchard as a liquid foliar spray.

The farm is managing a block of pear trees in Kodaikanal, which is at an altitude of 1800m (6000ft), which at that latitude means a temperate climate. All the preparation herbs grow here, and they are thus able to make all the biodynamic preparations.

This farm runs comprehensive seminars and field days which are a joy to be a part of. There are wonderful examples of cowhorns, all the preparations and the preparation flowers, cowpat pit, compost and compost heaps.

Because of the work involved this farm employs about 100 people in a wonderful holistic environment, and this of course supports all the employees' families. The social side of biodynamic farming is one of the most important dynamics, where there is a good interaction between people.

A journey into India with biodynamics

14

In the light of the previous chapters I would like to share my experiences working with biodynamic agriculture on the continent of India. This of course is a tropical continent which is vastly different in weather conditions and seasonal changes from that which I had been used to in the temperate countries such as New Zealand and Australia.

What I had to adjust to was the unfamiliar rhythm of the monsoon – to me, a totally new climate that delivers all the year's rainfall in the space of two or three months. People then have to get by with no rain for a period of nine months, and crops have to grow through the consequent drought. On top of this, temperatures are extremely hot, averaging 35°C and higher in the summer. There is a little relief in the winter months of December and January when average temperatures plummet to 25°C, sending people to wrap in their winter woollies. All this is no problem for the local farming population because this has been happening in India ever since India was, but for the *vadeshi* it is very different.

The monsoon, which should come to the western part of India in the middle of June, can be preceded by stifling hot temperatures of up to 45°C and even 50°C on the central plateau. Heavy rains through July and August ease off in September, with a cooling of the temperature. Then the monsoon sweeps up and over to the east to the Bay of Bengal, before returning down the southeastern coast in October and November with a similar temperature pattern.

The challenge was how to adapt to this weather pattern in relation to making the biodynamic preparations. Also, would it be possible to grow the preparation plants, which are from a temperate climate, in such a hot climate? It must be appreciated that all the indications given by Rudolf Steiner were related to middle-European countries. With no model to copy it was just a matter of going ahead and seeing what would happen.

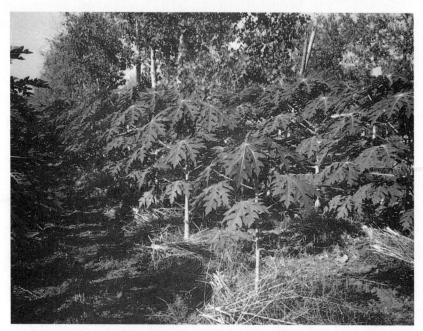

Papaya growing in Gujarat, India, mulched with cowpea,
a legume grown as a cover crop between rows.

It did seem obvious to start by making the cowhorn dung and to make it in the relatively cool time of the winter (November to February). Now the cow and its dung are highly venerated by the Indian people, so the concept of putting dung into a cowhorn and burying it in the earth struck a sympathetic chord in their farming philosophy. As the Indian proverbs say, 'The Goddess of Prosperity lives in cow dung', and 'In every cow live forty million gods'.

To get the cowhorns was not as easy as one might imagine. As the cow is sacred, most Indian people do not eat meat, so cows are rarely slaughtered. This means that one has to rely on natural death before the horns are available. There are literally millions of cows throughout India so there are always cows dying, and thus there is usually a plentiful supply in the yard where all the dead cows are taken.

Another difference from Western culture is the Indian farmer's custom of painting the cows' horns blue, red, green or yellow on festival occasions or during election times. This paint is usually scraped off before the dung is put into the horn.

Making the preparations

The first attempt at making the Preparation 500 at the Jawaharlal Nehru Krishi Viswa Vibyala (JNKVV) Agricultural University in Indore on the central plateau in Madhya Pradesh was not at all successful. This was incidentally exactly the same place that Sir Albert Howard in the 1930s made his now-famous 'Indore Compost' experiments. But for us it was the beginning of a very steep learning curve. Many wise heads, including Shri TGK Menon, Dr Khosla, Dr Schroff and Dr Trifale, thought about the problem which revolved around soil fertility and soil moisture. So the following year we used the same location but mixed compost with the existing soil in the pit before burying the horns. Also, we mulched quite heavily with paddy straw to keep the pit cool and well moistened during the winter dry period.

This time we were able to lift approximately 60 horns of very good 500 by New Zealand standards, after only four and a half months. Subsequently we have put several hundred horns successfully in other places in the Indore district and also in the south of India in the Madurai district in Tamil Nadu. There, in 1996, we successfully put down and lifted 3000 horns, recovering about 200kg of good cowhorn dung. In Indore we buried a further 26,000 horns. It is interesting to note that those very big horns from the Indian cattle with the large volume of manure

A farm near Ahmedabad, Gujarat, that has been biodynamic for two years.
Wheat production is now 50 percent greater than the neighbouring farm.
1 cu m of compost per acre and Preparation 500 were applied four times.

that they can contain seem to make excellent 500 in the warm climate. All the horns are filled by hand using fingers and thumbs. With the enthusiastic labour available, 3000 horns could be filled in about four hours.

Also at Indore, at the same time as the second attempt at making 500, we made preparations 502–506 in exactly the same way as they are made in New Zealand (see Chapter 7). Again, what about the animal parts that were needed? Well, back to the dead cow yard; and with the aid of Dr Solanki, a retired Ministry of Agriculture vet, we obtained the necessary parts from a young cow that had recently died from eating a plastic bag. The parts had to be used very quickly because of the number of flies and the rapid putrefaction in the extreme heat.

We added compost to the soil again, placed each of the preparations in an earthenware pot, and buried them separately 400mm deep. Just below the surface of the soil we put pieces of thornbush to discourage the wild dogs, and we put compost on top to encourage any worms to go there instead of into the preparation. The skull can be buried in a barrel near an irrigation pond or some wet spot.

All the compost preparations turned out very well and were duly stored in glass jars in a cool spot.

Cabbage, cauliflower and broccoli growing on a mixed
biodynamic farm in Anand, Gujurat, India.

We made Preparation 501 relatively easily from local quartz which occurs in geodes in the district around Indore. The quartz is ground to a fine meal in a mortar and pestle, made into a paste and buried in the good soil that has been described previously.

Soya bean trial at Indore Agricultural College

At Indore Agricultural College a trial growing soya beans has been carried out by Dr Khosla, comparing the effects of biodynamic preparations on soil and crop with the effects of conventional chemical fertiliser application. The trial area was divided into four 1-acre plots as follows:

Plot 1: treated with locally made 500 together with a small amount of
compost made with preparations 502–506, all of which had
been made at Indore, and Preparation 507 from New Zealand

Plot 2: treated with chemical fertiliser of 20N 60P 20K

Plot 3: treated with chemical fertiliser of 10N 30P 10K

Plot 4: the control.

Colour plate four shows the improved soil structure, root development and growth in the biodynamic plot 1 compared with the growth in the chemically fertilised plot 2 and in the control plot 4. No photo was made of plot 3.

The yield of the biodynamic plot 1 was 30 per cent higher than any of the other plots.

Another trial in the following season, this time using wheat, showed very similar results in relation to the soil structure and crop growth. It should be pointed out that the 500 had been sprayed just four months before the start of the trial.

Growing the preparation plants in India

I found that it was impossible to grow the preparation plants in the hot climate of the central plateau. As luck would have it, Kurinji Farms in the south, which grow mainly mangoes, have a pear orchard in the hills at 2000m, which has a much cooler temperature range than on the plains. Here we found dandelion and yarrow growing, and we introduced chamomile and nettle. Valerian is yet to be established but it is only a matter of time before that happens. The difficult one is the European oak: the only specimens are moss-covered and very weak-looking.

However, in the very north of India, in the foothills of the Himalayas around Nainital, we found an evergreen oak (*Quercus dilatata*) which has a very high calcium content in its bark, almost twice the percentage of *Q. robur*. We also found a perennial nettle (*Urtica parviflora*) which looks promising.

With both these areas in the north and the south it looks as if it will be possible to grow the plants we require for preparation-making. Biodynamic preparations can then be made in sufficient quantities to enable widespread adoption of biodynamic management in India.

More on India

The above was written in 1996, and now in 2004 work in biodynamic agriculture has gone along very well.

The horn dung, the horn silica and all the compost preparations with the exception of valerian are now being made in India in large quantities. In the areas of the hill country of Kodaikanal, near Palghat in Kerala and in the hills of Nainital in Uttaranchel, it still has not been possible to grow large quantities of valerian.

Working at a biodynamic tea garden, Nilgilri Hills, southwest India.

Many farmers all over India are making high-quality horn dung Preparation 500 and the horn silica 501. They are very particular about getting the dung from a lactating cow.

Another feature of the biodynamic work in India is the large quantities of excellent compost the farmers make.

A regular training programme, at Kodaikanal in south India, has taken place twice yearly since 1997. It is now run by the recently formed Biodynamic Association of India. There have so far been sixteen introductory training programmes, where probably a total of over 300 students from all over India and Sri Lanka have attended.

The courses cover the background and history of the biodynamic movement in the world. Then there is a very practical 'hands-on' introduction to the making of all the preparations and how to use them. Also covered are the making and use of compost, and the making of the cowpat pit and liquid manures in ways that are particularly applicable to Indian conditions.

Emphasis is laid on the maintenance of soil fertility and the use of green manuring.

Biodynamic farm in Anand, India, growing alfalfa for cattle feed. It is cut every three weeks, manured with cowpat pit compost and Preparation 500, and irrigated.

Also, each day time is given to becoming familiar with the cosmic rhythms and using the planting calendar. There are studies on astronomy and night sky observations.

A similar regular programme has been held in the autumn near Anand in Gujarat since 2000. This programme is held on a 40-acre fully biodynamic, well-managed mixed farm, and is attended by farmers from the west of India. This farm is a good place for a hands-on introductory seminar in biodynamics as there is a well-fed dairy herd supplying milk, and a wide range of vegetables and fruits. This is supported by an ongoing programme of making compost, CPP, liquid manures and Preparations 500 and 501.

Another centre is running similar courses on a biodynamic apple orchard in the district of Nainital, which is in the foothills of the Himalayas. As well as apples, they grow potatoes and tomatoes. This area grows the stinging nettle and the oak bark which is used for preparation-making in the rest of the country. The full range of the biodynamic preparations are made here and distributed to farmers in the north.

Students who have been through these courses are working on and have

Working in a tea garden, Assam.

helped convert tea estates, coffee gardens and market gardens, vanilla gardens, various tropical fruit, coconut, rice, wheat and dairy farms to biodynamic management. Generally these farms are growing very high quality produce which is now recognised more and more all over India by many consumers. Some of the farms are reaching the Demeter certification standard.

With the practical experience they have gained on their own farms some of the ex-students are now able to give training courses in biodynamics themselves. Some have taken up research work into biodynamic agriculture. Others have become consultants, and others are doing valuable work showing village farmers the way of biodynamic/organic farming.

Both central and state government agricultural departments are beginning to see the value of the biodynamic method as an organic farming method, and are starting to give support for conferences and workshops.

Biodynamic farming elsewhere | 15

Biodynamic agriculture has been practised in many European countries since Rudolf Steiner gave his Agriculture Lectures in 1924. Ehrenfried Pfeiffer took the impulse to the United States in the early 1950s. Biodynamic preparations were first applied in New Zealand in 1928.

The whole development of the technology of the biodynamic approach has taken place largely in the temperate zones of the world, perhaps with the thought that it would not be applicable to tropical or arid regions (presumably because Steiner did not mention tropical or arid countries in his lectures).

A great library of experience, both practical and theoretical, has been developed over the past seventy years in European countries, especially Germany, Holland, Switzerland and Sweden. Most countries have looked to Germany for a lead in this development — it is considered the cradle of the impulse for biodynamic agriculture. I have personally learned and gained a tremendous amount from giants of the movement such as Dr Herbert Koepf, who has written books and instigated informative scientific experiments on the subject (see Koepf, *The Biodynamic Farm*).

Another leading light is Maria Thun, who from her farm in Germany has, with great single-mindedness of research spanning forty years or more, pointed out to the agricultural world the effects of the cosmic workings in every thing growing. Her *Working on the Land and the Constellations* is written in such a way that farmers can use the basic information she gives to plan their own planting, sowing and harvesting times and to develop systems to suit the conditions on their farm.

Dr Jochen Bockemuhl, from the Natural Science Section of the Goetheanum in Switzerland, has presented a wonderful gift to students of the agricultural world with his observations of nature and studies of the metamorphosis of plants. His book, *In Partnership with Nature* (1981), opened up for me a whole new world of observations of plants and their connections with the cosmos, which is an integral part of the study of biodynamic agriculture.

Over the years in Germany, valuable work has been done in the making and the use of the preparations. Scientific experiments have also been carried out, and this has helped the credibility of the movement as well as the practical work of farmers (see Koepf, *The Biodynamic Farm*). The Demeter certification trademark set up in Germany in 1928 was the first production standard to be set up in the world, and one on which subsequent standards have been modelled.

I have visited quite a few biodynamic farms in Sweden, Holland, Austria, Switzerland and Germany; and there are farms in most other European countries as well. Generally the farms are smaller than those in the southern hemisphere, and probably make more intensive use of the land than New Zealand farms do. European farms typically run a produce shop which the farmer stocks with a wide range of goods such as flour, wholemeal bread, cheeses, quark, yoghurt, butter, milk, meats and small goods, all seasonal vegetables, fruits and berries, as well as fruit juices from other farms, so customers can buy nearly all their food there, and all of Demeter quality. What a joy — but what a pity they are not in every town in every country of the world!

There is now in Europe a growing awareness of the dangers posed by agricultural chemicals in the pollution of the environment. The organic agricultural movement as such is growing in popularity and people are looking for 'residue-free' products in the marketplace. Unfortunately most farmers are turning not to the biodynamic method but rather to the 'organic' methods that were practised in the 1920s. I hope this book has convinced the reader of the need to convert farms, not only to an organic system, but to the added dimension of biodynamics. I feel that there needs to be a renaissance not only in Europe but throughout the world, to present this new direction in agriculture to people everywhere.

We are now going through the changing of the guard. The pioneers are no longer there, and as always, there is a gap before the next generation takes over. I have met many farmers of the next generation in Europe: they are confident and enthusiastic, and they can understand the importance of the biodynamic approach and take it on into the future.

Eastern Europe

The Eastern bloc of Europe was starved of any biodynamic input during the communist regime. The only work I know of was carried out in Budapest in Hungary during the occupation by Clara Mezei, who made the preparations at home and distributed them secretly to friends for their home gardens. The Hungarian movement is now being established.

After the collapse of communism there have been a number of initiatives in most countries in the East. Poland has had biodynamic farms for more than five years now, and as in Estonia, Latvia and Lithuania, farmers are being helped by advisors from Sweden, Germany and Holland.

Work started in Russia over a decade ago, and since then a number of ventures have been set up with help from German, Canadian and American advisors. In the Ukraine, Moldavia, Georgia and Armenia things are beginning to happen, with preparations being made and applied. These countries are being helped by advisors from Germany and America.

Mediterranean

There is a large group of biodynamic farms in Egypt growing cotton. This is a very enthusiastic and successful venture.

A few small biodynamic farms exist in Israel. Preparations are being made and used in the arid areas of Tunisia; this initiative is being helped by advisors from Holland.

UK and Ireland

As yet there are very few biodynamic farms in the UK. The ones that are there are good. There has been a strong input there over the years since Steiner gave his original course, with an active biodynamic association working with great enthusiasm making the preparations, running field days and producing a newsletter. There is an active home-garden movement. For a number of years Herbert Koepf ran a biodynamic agricultural course at Emerson College, where many farmers and gardeners from all over the world learnt their biodynamics from him. In 2004 Emerson College is offering a wide range of short courses, and as well a four-year biodynamic course in conjunction with the Warmonderhof

Groenhurst College, Netherlands (for more information see the Emerson College website, www.emerson.org.uk). The biodynamic impulse has not taken off in the UK's mainstream agriculture. It is not as though biodynamics does not work in the UK, and there are some excellent examples of farms and gardens in the Camphill Homes throughout Britain, Wales and Scotland; in fact, the vegetable gardens are some of the best I have ever seen. (Camphill Homes are communities established to provide spiritual care, along the lines suggested by Rudolf Steiner. They were founded in Scotland shortly before the Second World War by Dr Karl Koenig, an Austrian student of Rudolf Steiner. There are now more than forty such homes in the UK and at least fifty in other countries throughout the world, and all have biodynamically run gardens and farms.)

Forest Row in Britain is the home of the Virbela flowform design and research. The forms, developed by John Wilkes, are making a tremendous impact on the mixing of biodynamic preparations and liquid manures the world over.

In Ireland there are a few farms and a very enthusiastic and lively association which should soon show positive results.

As with the rest of the world, I think the UK is ready for a biodynamic explosion, orchestrated largely by younger enthusiasts.

North America

A similar situation exists in the United States. As previously mentioned, Ehrenfried Pfeiffer did a huge amount of work during the 1950s setting up laboratories and research centres. Pfeiffer also developed a compost starter based on the compost preparations 502–507, which is still in existence, and which was used successfully in Oakland, California to break down municipal garbage wastes from 1950 to 1952. Unfortunately this impulse was 'leant on' by the fertiliser multinationals of the time and the operation was closed down. This was a great disappointment to Pfeiffer, and it dampened his enthusiasm for continuing the work.

At the present time most of the biodynamic activity in the US is on the west and east coasts; but overall there are relatively few farms, considering the size of the country. The preparation-making which is based in Virginia is of a high standard. There is a well-organised biodynamic association based in San Francisco, and nearby in Sacramento at Fair Oaks, close to a Rudolf Steiner school, biodynamic training programmes are being run. (For more information see their website: www.steinercollege.org/biodynamic.html.) In Maine there is a Virbela flowform research centre, and a research institute in East Troy in Wisconsin is working on the development of corn varieties and doing experiments on cowpat pit and the uses of preparations and flowforms. But again one wonders why, with the great examples of biodynamic agriculture in this country, there are not more people inspired to 'give it a go'.

In Canada there are a few committed farmers and an association with a huge potential for growth. It is tempting to imagine all the wheat in Canada being grown as Demeter, and the benefits to the millions of people who would eat bread made from this wheat.

In the Dominican Republic there is a very successful biodynamic grower of bananas, whose fruit tastes great and who is running seminars in biodynamic agriculture there.

South America

There is a biodynamic institute in Brazil at Botucatu which is the centre of a community project initiative. Here is a large mixed farm growing vegetables and herbs and also supplying milk to a milk-processing factory. In the same district there are several smaller farms, which are growing maize, beans, rice, vegetables, and grassland for dairy cows. Close by is a Rudolf Steiner school and a cultural centre where biodynamic farmers are trained.

The Pacific Rim

Work has started on the development of biodynamic farming systems in the Philippines, Japan, Malaysia, Singapore and Hawaii.

Australia

Robert Williams was the Australian biodynamic pioneer who perfected the preparation-making in the late 1930s and 40s and shared his knowledge with his Australian colleagues and with their New Zealand cousins across the Tasman.

There are now two biodynamic associations in Australia — one in Victoria and the other in northern New South Wales. Both associations are very active and support a large number of farms throughout the whole of Australia, growing a wide range of crops, including grains, fine wool and lambs, beef, subtropical and tropical fruits, nuts, citrus, and a full range of vegetables and herbs. The Australian farming scene is very diverse, with growing conditions ranging from tropical country in the north growing crops such as bananas, to arid outback sheep-country, to highly productive market gardens and orchards on the eastern coast and in the south.

Biodynamic agriculture has reached a high level of expertise over the years, with both associations making good quality preparations to distribute to their members. They also offer advisory services. There are regular field days and seminars, especially in the eastern areas. Many farms are encouraged to make their own Preparation 500, with emphasis on quality.

Update on the Biodynamic Farming and Gardening Association, Australia

In 2003 this association changed its name to Biodynamic AgriCulture Australia. The new name reflects a surge of interest in biodynamic agriculture in all parts of Australia. This association runs regular educational programmes of seminars and workshops virtually all over the continent, which until recently have been supported by State funding under a 'Farm Biz' scheme which subsidises the costs of farming education. The association has made the most of this scheme, with the result that very many Australian farmers are practising biodynamics.

Australia, as we know, is a very large continent and consequently as more farmers are becoming interested in taking up biodynamic agriculture there is a need for large amounts of the biodynamic preparations. This association, along with many farmers, is now making large quantities of the preparations. Much effort is directed by the biodynamic association towards maintaining a very high standard of preparation making and application, and it has begun biennial master-class preparation courses for those farmers wishing to make their own preparations. The association makes the preparations available to all members.

Being conscious of the huge area of land that may require the preparations in the future, the council sees the need to limit the amount of Preparation 500 used. They have noted the success that New Zealand BD farmers have had on large areas using smaller quantities of Preparation 500.

The Australian association is now recommending using less horn dung Preparation 500 on large farms. The rate is 15g of 500 for large farms, together with 150g of manure concentrate (cowpat pit), 10g of horn clay and 5ml of fermented equisetum 10x in 33 litres of water per hectare. Up to 2700 litres (enough for approximately 80 hectares) can be stirred in a Virbela vortex flow-form and applied either by Land Cruiser or aircraft.

On smaller farms cowhorn dung 500 is used at the rate of 25g, plus the manure concentrate, horn clay and equisetum, per hectare. (For more information see the Biodynamic AgriCulture Australia Resource Manual.) The association also publishes four issues of its very lively newsletter, *Newsleaf*, per year.

This brief summary of biodynamic activity around the world gives some idea of how widespread this impulse is. It is small as yet; but as always, a seed must be sown before a tree can grow.

Conclusion: why biodynamic agriculture?   16

Biodynamic agriculture is a system of organic agriculture that has proved to be very effective throughout the world. The results are better soils, quality food, healthy plants, healthy and contented animals, and enthusiastic farmers and consumers.

It's not as if it's a fly-by-night idea that has no basis for reality. It's happening and has been for eighty years!

The world is slowly becoming aware of the problems of pollution facing humanity, particularly in the agricultural field. Entrepreneurs see a market for selling food that has been grown with fewer pollutants, but still with the downstream adverse effects on the environment. There is a growing movement of farmers who are genuinely trying to grow organically; but often they are only replacing the chemical inputs of the conventional grower with organic inputs. It is still the same basic understanding of growing: input = output.

In contrast, biodynamic techniques enhance, rejuvenate, add to and maintain soil quality. Cowhorns and cow dung, after being buried together in the earth, make the most wonderful humus to spread on the land. This improves the structure of the soil dramatically and quickly. Good soil structure means better water-holding capacity, which means better control, with consequently less loss of topsoil, which means better and deeper roots and less need for irrigation, which means deeper soil and more natural fertility.

We know that the earth is tired and overstressed. People have been taking and taking for years and not putting anything back. Now, through biodynamic farming, we have the chance to change this.

So what's the problem?

1   Cowhorns — people don't understand what these have to do with growing crops.

2   Because this concept is different from what is considered the norm, people think it must therefore be wrong.

3   People ask, 'How can such a small amount have such an effect? Have you had it scientifically tested?'

Earth fertility and food quality

The farmers of India have no problem in understanding the majesty of the cow in relationship to the continuance of fertility of the earth. They realise the cow is a gift from heaven.

Indian agriculture has a history of 4000 years. Indian farmers recognise the connection of the divine in the growing of food, and have done for years. We in the West prefer to turn our back on help from on high. We think we can do it all ourselves, and that we are the masters of creation.

People of Western cultures are generally interested in quantity of production rather than quality. This is a greedy attitude, but one admired and applauded by the lords of economic performance. When applied to the growing of food, this attitude is justified by the need to feed a hungry world. Unfortunately, it is beginning to rub off on Asian people as well.

It can be done

It is possible to grow sufficient food for the world without poisoning our planet. We do not need to use a whole array of chemicals and synthetic materials. The use of hybridised or genetically engineered seeds is totally unnatural and unnecessary (see Chapter 10).

Biodynamic technology, with its informed use of the various preparations, will maintain soil fertility for years to come in a wholly natural way. It will support the growing of a plentiful supply of nourishing food. In India it has been shown that soya beans grown using biodynamic methods produce 30 per cent more crop than those that are chemically grown.

At some point in considering our existence in this world, most people come to a recognition that there is a higher power than ourselves that is responsible for creation; that there is a force of growth, albeit a beneficent one. Nature provides us with examples of this life force every day, in the mighty trees of the forest, in scented roses, a medicinal herb, a nourishing carrot or a blade of grass.

This is where we must grasp the nettle in our attempt to understand biodynamic agriculture and to make the connection between this force of growth and the use of the biodynamic preparations.

The preparations are made from all-natural products — cow dung, quartz, and medicinal herbs — and are processed in conjunction with various animal parts. These preparations, when applied to the soil through ground sprays, composts and liquid manures, enliven the soil. They make happen all the biological soil processes, referred to in Chapter 3, that soil scientists talk about but rarely see in the field (see Reganold *et al.*, 1993).

Another thing that biodynamic farmers take into consideration is that the heavenly bodies and the fixed stars in their constellations play a very important role in the continuance of life on our planet. This is the basis of biodynamic agriculture.

Steiner gave the world ideas on a renewal of agriculture. He pointed out that we must nourish the earth in such a way that the cosmic influences could continue to flow in. During his lectures, the idea for the use of the biodynamic preparations was born.

Using the biodynamic preparations regularly opens the soil and the land to the effects of cosmic activities and allows these to work through the soil into the plants. The more biologically active the earth, the more the beneficent forces can work through into plant and animal.

Human beings, consumers of these plants and animal products, gain in forces to develop the right thinking, a healthy life of feeling, and a strong will to do so, when eating the food that is grown in this enlivened environment.

These concepts are beautifully simple, logical and easy to understand if people have the right mindset. There are no hidden agendas here. Recognition of this renewal of agriculture has to come about.

- ◎ It's all about our drinking water — its purity and its quality.

- ◎ It's about quality food.

- ◎ It's about the social life on farms all over the world.

- It's about an affordable, sustainable system of agriculture that will allow all farmers to stay on their land for many years.

- It's about farming being the most important activity in the world.

- It makes organic agriculture work!

- In my opinion it will only be biodynamic agriculture and all that emanates from it, that can give the world the spiritual hope and confidence for the future that we are all looking for.

Think about it.

Appendix 1

Storage and use of the biodynamic preparations

Preparation 500

Quantities to use

The stirred preparations are applied at the rate of 25g of 500 in 13 litres (3 gallons) per acre or 65g in 33 litres per hectare. All preparations should be applied within one hour of stirring, so only mix up the amount you can apply in an hour. This amount depends on the method of application and whether you have friends to help.

Multiply the number of acres you can cover in an hour by 13.5 to find out how many litres of preparation to stir. For example:

- ⊚ if you and your friends can walk over 7 acres of land in an hour,
  then the most preparation to stir at a time is 7 x 13.5 = 94.5 litres.

- ⊚ If you can cover 50 acres with a tractor and spray rig per hour,
  then stir 50 x 13.5 = 675 litres at one time.

Stirring equipment and how to stir

For up to 1 acre of land

Up to 13 litres can be comfortably stirred by hand with a small stick. Stir while resting your elbows on your knees. To make a good vortex requires a wristy movement. Start slowly at the edge of the bucket and move into the centre, increasing the stirring speed. When a crater appears in the water, break it by stirring in the opposite direction.

You can change hands when changing direction, and it is easier to always stir outward, ie with the right hand clockwise and with the left hand anticlockwise. There should be about three direction changes a minute.

For 1–10 acres of land

Up to 130 litres can be stirred using a 200-litre plastic drum or an oak barrel, with a 1.3–1.6m long 2.5cm diameter wooden rod, suspended by means of a nylon cord tied firmly to an overhanging branch, beam or a tripod of stout poles. The rod is tied so that it swings 7cm above the bottom of the barrel. The rod thus takes all the weight and makes the stirring and creating of the vortex relatively easy.

For 10–200 acres

A rotating paddle system, driven by a 1hp electric motor, can be used to stir 140–230 litres
– enough to do 10–16 acres at a time. The motor is connected to timing and reversing
switch gear, which enables the direction of rotation to alternate just as a hand-stirrer
would. The vortex should develop as quickly as possible with this size machine, usually
taking 30–45 seconds. There should be a 6- to 10-second delay before the opposite rotation
begins. Set the time switch to 30–45 seconds on and 6–10 seconds off.

For 200–500 acres

A hydraulic motor is needed to stir 450–1400 litres. The motor is linked up to the hydraulic
system of a tractor at 10hp or more. The reversing and timing switch gear is run off the
tractor's 12-volt system.

Virbela flowforms

There are five types of Virbela flowform cascades available for mixing fertilisers, which are
also suitable for stirring Preparations 500 and 501:

- The Jaerna, which stirs up to 900 litres in an hour
- The Beehive, which stirs up to 900 litres in an hour
- The Herten, which stirs up to 1800 litres in an hour
- The VB500, which stirs up to 2700 litres in an hour
- The Vortex, which stirs up to 2700 litres in an hour

The movement that water makes as it passes through the flowform cascade is one of
alternating vortices. This is very similar to the succession of vortices produced in a bucket
or a barrel while stirring, except that you can see the whole succession laid out in front of
you at once. The vortices, however, occur one after another, just as they do in a bucket,
because the water flows from a clockwise-rotating chamber into an anticlockwise one, and
so on.

A cascade always has a separate 'entry' form at its head, which sets up the right
conditions for water entering the system. With a cascade of seven Jaerna forms (plus entry
form) it is possible to stir up to 550 litres in one hour. With 7–14 (plus one) VB500 forms
it is possible to stir up to 2700 litres in one hour. At the moment a high-volume, low-
pressure pump is used to circulate the water continuously for an hour. Other pumps with
a softer action are being investigated.

Water

Rainwater is preferable and, in areas of little pollution, can be collected off the roofs of
houses, woolsheds and hay barns. It can be stored in concrete, galvanised iron or untreated
wooden tanks.

If spring water is used, it should be checked for pollutants and chemical residues. If found to be clean, it should stand in the light and air for two days, as it may have been underground for many years. River water should likewise be checked for purity.

Heating water

Water for stirring should be between 25° and 30°C, and it is best heated with a natural heat such as a flame or sunlight. Suitable heaters are butane or woodburners and solar panels. An old-fashioned copper or a 44-gallon steel drum over a fire or burner, or a Marshall (Thermette-type) heater are satisfactory.

Spraying of Preparation 500

This is best done in the afternoon, in autumn or early spring and while the moon is in a descending phase (see planting calendar). It is best to cover your land in an ingoing spiral, starting from the outside, rather than to zig-zag back and forth.

Hand application

For small areas use a hearth brush (not nylon). Dip the brush into the stirred 500, and spread the liquid using an action similar to a backhand tennis stroke with an upward movement as you walk along. This will spread large droplets over a width of about 10 metres.

Wheeled vehicles

Larger areas of 20 acres or more can be sprayed with a tractor, using a centrally mounted three-jet nozzle, which will give 9–18m of coverage at a pressure of 20–40psi, created by a rotary or diaphragm pump. A long boom spray is too unwieldy, and of no advantage.

Another arrangement is the four-wheel-drive farm bike towing a trailer with a 450-litre tank. A centrifugal pump, electrically driven from the bike's battery, provides the spraying power. You can expect such an arrangement to cover 20–30 acres per hour on flat land. On hilly country saddle tanks can be fitted to the bike, using the same pump and nozzle system. It is also possible to fit a spray gun which will reach inaccessible slopes and gullies.

In easy, rolling country a four-wheel-drive utility such as a Land Rover can be used. You can mount a 900-litre tank on such a vehicle, with a small petrol motor to drive a diaphragm pump, again with the centrally mounted three-jet nozzle. It is often possible to cover 60–70 acres an hour with such a rig.

Nozzles for spraying Preparation 500 are best mounted low to the ground. There are several sources of suitable jets (Spraying Systems Co. makes one called Boom Jet Nozzle or contact Biodynamic AgriCulture Australia), or you can make your own. The spray gear should be run at a pressure of 20–40psi.

An efficient spray tank trailer with an independent pump, mounted with a single spray nozzle with pressure adjustment, suitable for both Preparations 500 and 501. It can be towed by a 4WD farm bike.

Aircraft

Aircraft need to have four open-ended nozzles along a boom fixed to each wing or under the helicopter. An air-driven pump feeding off a 900-litre hopper tank completes the arrangement. Since an aircraft can spread 900 litres in about fifteen minutes, you need to stir 2700 litres at a time, and store the remaining 1800 litres. The stirring machine or flowform can then be used for mixing the next batch while the first batch is being applied. An 1800-litre black plastic tank is suitable.

You may have noticed that these calculations seem to have 'lost' fifteen minutes out of the hour. The time will be used by the operator in loading and taxiing. But if the airstrip is distant from the paddock, you may have to adjust these figures, and stir smaller batches to allow for the increased flying time.

One logistical problem of aerial spraying is the large volume of rainwater needed. For example, for a 1000-acre farm, you will need 13,600 litres (3000 gallons) of water. A bit of thought is necessary to work out a system of water-collection facilities, and cartage by tanker or pipe to the airstrip, and the warming once it is there.

One farmer has an ideal setup. His woolshed, with its large roof catchment area, is quite close to, but higher than, the airstrip. Thus, gravitational supply of water to the airstrip is possible. The advantage of using a helicopter is that it does not need a runway, so it can go to where the water is stored and mixed.

It is important that the aircraft spraying system is clean and free of pollutants. (A contaminated tank can be cleaned with bleach, followed by a thorough rinse.) Some farmers form a syndicate which owns the pump, boom and liner for the tank. In the future it is possible that there will be aircraft operators who work only with biodynamic farmers.

Spraying of Preparation 501

This is best done early in the morning, in spring during an ascending period of the moon or when the moon and Saturn are in opposition. It can also be done when the crop is almost mature, but spraying 501 while the crop is still developing is likely to cause it to hasten into maturity. This may lead, for example, to beautifully formed but very small lettuces.

When spraying, observe how far the spray mist is carried by any wind movement. You can make the next pass over the garden or paddock at the point that the spray drift has reached. You can adjust your travelling speed according to the wind movement – on a very still morning you will travel or walk back and forth (not spiral) across the land more quickly than on a day when the wind is carrying the spray mist a good distance.

Small areas should be done with a knapsack sprayer. Use a fine nozzle and direct the spray up into the air. It is possible to get an extension arm for the nozzle to enable the 501 to be sprayed higher up into the air, for instance on fruit trees. Do not use a motorised knapsack sprayer as the exhaust fumes may interfere with the 501.

Larger areas can be covered using the same machinery as described for spraying Preparation 500. The main differences are that the pressure should be much higher (80–100psi), and the nozzle jets should be changed to a smaller aperture, creating a fine mist which is allowed to drift – wind direction (if not too strong) can be used to advantage.

General points about equipment

If you are buying equipment for spraying or stirring preparations, consider other possible uses for it. The most likely use is the mixing or spreading of liquid fertiliser.

Be careful of old or secondhand equipment – you need to be certain it has not been used for herbicides or other agricultural chemicals.

Storing preparations

If the preparations are not used immediately after receiving them, or if you find it more convenient to have a stock on hand, they should be stored in a suitable container to prevent the loss of the vital life forces.

Preparations 502–507 are best placed in small glass jars or glazed earthenware pots with loose-fitting lids. The five jars or pots as well as the bottle of valerian should be stored in a box which is well insulated with peat or sphagnum moss. To make such a box, place a small box within a large one, and pack the peat or sphagnum between the two. The sphagnum should be dry.

The lid of the storage box should be also insulated. For this, use a sandwich construction of peat or sphagnum between two 10mm boards. Make sure the wood used in the box construction is untreated.

Check regularly that the preparations are moist enough, and if not, add a small amount of rainwater — half a teaspoon may be all that is needed in the case of compost preparations. Remember the preparations are living, so they need a little air: do not screw the lids down tight.

When your preparations are well stored they develop a life of their own, and you will notice bacterial deposits like small worm castings on the sides of the jars.

Preparation 500 can be stored in glass jars (eg Agee) or glazed earthenware pots with loose-fitting lids or corks, and placed in a storage box as described above, or surrounded by peat and sphagnum in a box.

The boxes with the Preparations 500 and 502–507 should be kept in a cool place, not in direct sunlight, and not in a refrigerator or coolstore. A suitable place would be under a house. Avoid contamination by petrol and oil fumes.

Preparation 501 is stored in a glass jar with a very loose lid in the sunlight — for example on a sunny windowsill.

Application of Compost Preparations 502-507

There are excellent descriptions of the preparations in the book *Biodynamics*, prepared by the New Zealand BioDynamic Association (pp 106–29), and in Pearce, *A Biodynamic Farmer's Handbook* (pp 20–23).

To compost heap

One set of compost Preparations 502–507 is sufficient to treat up to 5 cubic metres of compost. If you make your compost in the home garden in a bin or a small windrow-type pile which may be only 1 cubic metre in volume, you will still use one complete set.

If you make more compost, say in a long windrow-type pile 2 metres wide at the base and 1.5 metres high, you will need one set of preparations for every 5 metres of pile length. After allowing for pile shrinkage you will have approximately 1 cubic metre of compost per metre of length.

To insert Preparations 502–506, take a small handful of mature compost from a previous heap, some well-rotten cow manure, or something similar. Fold this around each preparation to make a loose ball, and insert the preparations into five holes along the side of the heap. The holes can be made with a crowbar or shovel handle.

Valerian Preparation 507 should be mixed with warmed rainwater for ten minutes. One portion of preparation (10ml) goes into 13.5 litres of water, of which half is poured into two holes in the top of the heap. The remainder is sprinkled over the completed compost heap. Steiner pointed out that as soon as the preparations are inserted, the forces they carry radiate throughout the heap.

To liquid fertilisers

To insert the compost preparations into liquid fertilisers, put the preparations into the small amount of compost as previously described, and 'float' the compost on the top of the liquid.

The 507 can be stirred for ten minutes in a small quantity (about 1 litre) of water, and poured into the liquid.

To cowpat pit

Make five holes, 3cm deep, on the top of the manure. Insert one portion each of Preparations 502–506, and cover the holes. Pour half the stirred valerian into another hole in the dung, and sprinkle the rest over the bricks and hessian sack. You may wish to reprepare the dung after the first turning.

Appendix 2
Checklist for making Preparation 500

1   The cow dung for Preparation 500 should come from lactating certified cows grazing on or fed from fodder from a biodynamic farm.

2   Avoid concentrates. The manure should be free of obvious impurities such as grass, stones, earth, bark, etc.

3   The horns used must be cowhorns, not bullhorns. (Cowhorns can be distinguished from bullhorns by their annular calving rings and solid tips.)

4   The horns should be buried in soil that displays obvious biological activity. (In practice this means soil that has been regularly treated with the biodynamic preparations and biodynamic compost for at least three full years.) Good results have been obtained by burying the horns in soil mixed with 50 per cent mature biodynamic compost. Make sure the horns are not touching and the soil is well firmed around each horn.

5   Do not bury horns in land that becomes waterlogged.

6   The horns must be buried in the living topsoil layer, ideally at a depth of 30cm.

7   The horns must stay in the soil for at least six months, from autumn to spring, except in tropical countries.

8   The resultant Preparation 500 should have changed into a sweet-smelling, earthy, highly colloidal, reasonably firm condition.

9   The resultant Preparation 500 should also be free from impurities. Particular care should be taken when lifting, not to mix in soil or other foreign matter.

10 The preparation should be transferred immediately to storage in a cool place, in properly insulated containers. The storage area should be away from direct sunlight and free of airborne contaminants such as diesel and petrol fumes, paint flakes and so on.

Appendix 3

Timetable for making and applying preparations
in different parts of the world

These calendars provide a rough guide for beginners. For successful biodynamic management, farmers need to develop a 'feel' for when is the right time to apply the preparations for their particular farm and climate.

In hot countries the fermentation time for all preparations will be shorter than in temperate climates: in warmer climates it will take four to five months; in cooler climates, six to seven months.

Table A1: A calendar for making and using Preparation 500

Action	New Zealand and temperate Australia	India, tropical Australia and Asia	Europe, northern United States and Canada	California and Mediterranean
Bury	April	Oct/Nov	Sept/Oct	Nov
Lift	late Sept	Feb/Mar	Mar/May	Mar/Apr
Apply [1]				
in spring	Sept/Nov	Feb	late May/early Jun [2]	April
in autumn	Mar/May	Oct/Nov [3]	Aug [4]	Oct/Nov

[1] Apply during descending moon.
[2] Apply when soil temperature rises.
[3] Apply after the last monsoon rains.
[4] Apply before soil temperature falls.

Table A2: A calendar for making and using Preparations 501–508

Prep	Year	Spring	Late spring/summer	Autumn
501		bury horn		dig up horn
502	1	make & hang	harvest & wilt flowers	take down & bury
	2	dig up		
503[1]	1		harvest & dry flowers	make & bury
	2	dig up		
504	1		harvest foliage	bury
	2			dig up
505	1			gather bark, make & put in water
	2	retrieve		
506[2]	1		harvest & dry flowers	make & bury
	2	dig up		
507			harvest flowers & make	
508		harvest & dry		

[1] In most countries the flowers can be harvested and the preparation made in the late spring. Where flowers are unavailable by late spring, gather them the previous year, dry and store.

[2] You could also try making it the previous spring and hanging it in a tree for six months, as for Preparation 502.

Note: compost, liquid manures and cowpat pit can be made, and the compost preparations added to them, at any time of the year, although decomposition is quickest during the warmer months of the year. Steiner suggests hanging up the Preparations 503 and 506 (*Agriculture*, p 255).

Appendix 4
Understanding the planting calendar
— southern hemisphere

Biodynamic agriculture works from two poles — the cosmic and the earthly. Understanding and using the rhythms of the cosmos for sowing and planting in conjunction with the practice of soil fertility, already described, makes organic farming truly work.

The information in this appendix should be used in conjunction with the planting calendars produced by the biodynamic associations of New Zealand or Australia. The moon, solar, planetary, and constellation rhythms that are considered when working with the planting and sowing calendar are described below.

Full moon

Waxing (new to full) and waning (full to new) occurs approximately every 29.5 days.

1   In the 48 hours leading up to full moon there appears to be a distinct increase in the moisture content of the earth. The growth forces of the plants seem to be enhanced.

2   The full moon period is connected with the growth tendency of the plant, with quick germination of seeds, fast growth and a rapid regrowth of any cut, mown or pruned vegetation.

3   There appears to be quicker cell division and a tendency to elongation of growth.

4   Seed germination is fast but may be soft and prone to fungus attack, particularly in warm conditions and high humidity.

5   The influence of the full moon appears to provide favourable conditions for the growth of fungus on all plants. This is related to the increase in moisture and humidity.

6   There is an increase in insect activity, particularly slugs and snails, and internal worm parasites in humans and animals.

7   These conditions allow good absorption of liquid manures.

8   There is often a tendency for rain at full moon.

Activities connected with the full moon

1 Sow seeds at times of low humidity and warmth (48 hours before).

2 Apply liquid manures (48 hours before).

3 Fungus control — spray with equisetum tincture or D5 potency, or sodium silicate 0.5 per cent.

4 Insect control. Watch out for chewing and sucking insects. Look at using a garlic/ginger/chilli pepper spray, natural pyrethrum or neem oil. Watch out for slugs and snails. Surround plants with diatomaceous earth

Drench animals for internal parasites 48 hours before, on an empty stomach, with, for example, garlic and cider vinegar.

Activities connected with the new moon

1 Avoid sowing seeds.

2 Fell timber.

3 Traditional Indian agriculture recognised the day before new moon as No Moon Day, a day on which no agricultural work was done.

Moon and Saturn in opposition

This occurs every 27.5 days. Basically it is when the moon and Saturn are standing on opposite sides of the earth and their forces are raying in to the earth from each direction.

The moon forces bring in the calcium processes which are connected to propagation and growth forms, while the Saturn forces bring in the silica processes which are connected to building up substance in root, leaf and fruit. The balancing effect of these two influences streaming into the earth produces very strong plants from seed sown at this time.

Also it has been found that spraying with 501 (horn silica) at this time strengthens the plant to the extent that it can resist plant diseases and certain insect attack.

Activities connected with the moon opposite Saturn

1 Seed sowing and transplanting.

2 Spray with 501 in the very early morning on the day or the day before the aspect for fungus; for example, mildew and botrytis on grapes, rust on oats, mildew on tamarillos, greasy spot on passionfruit, mildew on cucurbits. Note: 501 is not a fungicide but it strengthens the plant to help it overcome the fungus.

Ascending and descending of the moon

The moon's daily path across the sky as seen from the earth is not always the same. Sometimes it is higher in the sky, sometimes lower, similar to the sun during its yearly cycle from summer to winter, except that the moon goes through this cycle every 27.3 days. The sun passes in front of the twelve zodiac constellations during the course of the year — from Gemini to Sagittarius (midwinter to midsummer), which is ascending, and from Capricorn to Taurus (midsummer to midwinter), descending.

We see the moon moving in an arc from east to west. When we see these arcs getting higher every day, the moon is *ascending* and when we see them getting lower every day the moon is *descending*. So as the moon takes 27.3 days to complete this cycle, each ascending and descending period lasts about two weeks.

The effects of the ascending and descending period can be compared to the gestures presented by the seasons. An *ascending* period is much like the *spring and summer* of the year — the earth 'breathes out'. We see this as an outpouring of growth activity above the soil surface. Growth forces and saps flow upwards more strongly and fill the plant with vitality. Although germination takes place below the ground, it also takes part in this upward striving. This is the time to spray Preparation 501.

The *descending* period, on the other hand, is related to the activity below the soil surface and can be compared with the *autumn/winter* of the year. The earth 'breathes in' and draws growth forces back down below the soil surface. The lower parts of the plant, especially the roots, are activated. This is the time for cultivation, composting and planting, also the time to apply Preparation 500.

Activities connected with ascending and descending

Ascending period

1   *Sow* all seeds. Use the appropriate constellation. For example:
>   for cereals: warmth constellation — Leo (lion);
>   for fruits: warmth constellation — Sagittarius (archer);
>   for leaf: water constellation — Cancer (crab), Scorpio (scorpion);
>   for flower: air/light constellation — Gemini (twins), Libra (scales);
>   for roots: earth constellation — Virgo (virgin).

2   *Spray* with 501 at early stages of growth when the plant is recognisable, and using the appropriate constellation, as above.

3   *Harvest* on an air/light constellation, Gemini (twins) or Libra (scales):
>   fruit and vegetables (not roots);
>   plants for making medicines, and biodynamic preparations;
>   flowers and plants for preparation-making;
>   field crops, eg silage and hay.

Descending period

1   Spray Preparation 500 in the afternoon, in autumn and early spring.
    The soil should be warm.

2   Make and spread compost.

3   Transplant seedlings and trees.

4   Make and plant cuttings.

5   Cultivate soil.

6   Harvest root crops for storage on an earth day, eg Taurus (bull).

7   Prune all fruit trees in the appropriate season on a fruit day,
    eg Aries (ram).

8   Prune flowering trees and shrubs and roses at the appropriate season
    on a flowering day, eg Aquarius (water bearer).

Nodes

These occur every 13.6 days. As the moon ascends and descends across the path of the sun, moon nodes occur at the point where the moon's path crosses the path of the sun. The influence of the node lasts for approximately six hours on either side of the node. The moon will negate the benefits of the sun's influence for this brief period, *so avoid* any *agricultural* or *horticultural* work.

The effect is similar to that of an eclipse of the sun by the moon.

Apogee and perigee

These occur every 27.5 days. The moon moves around the earth in an ellipse. The moon's nearest point to the earth on the ellipse is the perigee, and the furthermost point is the apogee. At apogee appears to be a good time to plant potatoes as there seems to be always a multiplicity of form (meaning more potatoes), whereas at perigee there are less potatoes but they are bigger.

At perigee, the time when the moon is closest to the earth, *greater moisture* is brought to the earth, and there is a tendency towards fungal growth.

Apogee and perigee times bring a stress period and seed sowing should be avoided twelve hours either side of these times (except potato planting at apogee).

Moon in zodiac constellations

The zodiac is a belt of fixed stars which are in a grouping which we call constellations. This belt ranges behind the ecliptic path, which is the path of the sun. All the planets, and the moon, move in front of the zodiac constellations. Here we are concerned with the moon, which passes in front of the complete circle of the constellations every 27.3 days. Because the constellations are of different sizes, the moon stands in front of each for between 1.5 and 3.5 days. The different constellations engender certain conditions that are favourable to the plants, which the moon will focus as it passes in front of these fixed stars. The effects are shown in the table at the top of the page opposite.

The influences of the particular constellation are brought into the soil through cultivation of the soil at the appropriate time, and also by the spraying of 501.

The germinating seed also receives these influences, so if it is desired to promote certain influences one cultivates and sows the seed during the favourable constellation period.

Moon in front of Virgo (virgin)	Capricorn (goat)	Taurus (bull)	Root development
Moon in Gemini (twins)	Libra (scales)	Aquarius (waterman)	Flower development
Moon in Cancer (crab)	Scorpio (scorpion)	Pisces (fishes)	Leaf development
Moon in Sagittarius (archer)	Aries (ram)		Fruit development
Moon in Leo (lion)			Seed development

Activities connected to moon rhythms

500 application

During a *descending* period, in the afternoon, in the spring or autumn.

501 application

During an *ascending* period at the beginning of the plant's growth and later just before harvest, or close to the moon's opposition to Saturn so as to bring quality, particularly in taste and keeping quality, and also to strengthen the plant against fungus.

Seed sowing

The following times have been found to be beneficial:

1   Moon opposite Saturn;

2   Full moon 48 hours before;

3   During an *ascending* period (avoid node, apogee, perigee, new moon);

4   Sow at the following times for the particular constellation effect on the
    ascending period:

> *Air light* flower
> — Gemini (twins)
> — Libra (scales)
>
> *Water* leaf
> — Cancer (crab)
> — Scorpio (scorpion)
>
> *Warmth* fruits
> — Sagittarius (archer)
>
> *Warmth* seeds
> — Leo (lion)
>
> *Earth* roots
> — Virgo (virgin)

Compost making

Best during *descending* period.

Compost spreading

Spread during the *descending* period in autumn or early spring, depending on soil
conditions and crop requirements.

Cultivation and soil preparation

Best during the *descending* period where weather and soil conditions permit. Note:
cultivation and working the soil when it is wet can cause structural damage.

Transplanting seedlings, container-grown plants, trees and shrubs

At the *descending* period at the appropriate season.

Harvesting

Generally we have found that all crops keep better and maintain quality in storage if
harvested during an *air/light period* on the *ascending* moon (Gemini (twins) or Libra
(scales)), eg fruit, green vegetables, hay and silage.

   Avoid harvesting at full moon, perigee and leaf day (Cancer (crab) and Scorpio
(scorpion)) as these are times of more water in the earth, and the crops would hold too
much water for satisfactory storage.

If seeds are to be saved, or grains harvested, choose a period when the moon is in Leo (lion).

Roots and potatoes should be harvested in a *descending* period when the moon is in an earth constellation, eg Taurus (the bull).

Liquid manure application

The best time is just before full moon, in the afternoon. Liquid manures can be used several times during the growth of the crop.

Plant potatoes

At apogee. Usually at this time good numbers of medium-size potatoes are produced. Also there is often a resistance to the potato tuber moth.

Fungus control

Full moon and perigee

These are stress times because they bring a watery influence to the earth and can lead to fungus attack, especially during warm weather from spring to autumn.

Spray with equisetum on the days prior to and during these times.

Spray with 501 in the early morning when the *moon is opposite Saturn*, which will strengthen the plant to resist the fungus.

Pruning

Prune all *fruit trees and berry shrubs* at the *descending* moon at the appropriate season. If possible choose a warmth constellation, eg Aries (ram), which will encourage fruit bud formation.

Prune all *flowering shrubs and roses* in the appropriate season at the *descending* moon. If possible choose an air/light day, eg Aquarius (waterman).

Other astronomical rhythms which appear on the planting calendar

Sun

One point in knowing the sun's position in the zodiac is its importance for the peppering of insects.

Other aspects

The positions of the planets (and the moon) in relationship to one another are shown on the calendars. This can be useful in determining and studying weather patterns.

It is useful to make notes of each day's weather and to check with the various planets' position in the constellations.

Planets

The planets' positions in front of the zodiac is shown, and this can be useful to people interested in astronomy.

Times

The time is shown using the 24-hour clock. For example, FM 1530 means 3.30pm; 10 means 10am.

In the New Zealand biodynamic calendar no adjustment is made for daylight saving.

Peppering

The following are guidelines for those interested in using the methods of peppering to reduce the incidence of weeds, insects and rodents as indicated by Rudolf Steiner.

Weeds

Seeds which are ripe and viable should be burnt at full moon or when the moon is in Leo. The seeds are placed in a small tin and put in a very hot fire. The resultant ash is spread over the land or potentised to D6 or D8, and should be spread at full moon, perhaps several times in the year.

Insects

Insects are burnt in a similar way to weeds but here they are burnt at the various constellations of the *sun*. The effect ranges from when the sun is in Aquarius to when the sun is in Cancer.

One needs to know the life cycle of the particular insect, and then determine in which environment it spends the most time; eg the grass grub spends most of its life in the earth, so one would choose an earth constellation, for instance Taurus. The common house fly or mosquito spends most of its life in a watery environment in the larval stage, so one would choose a water constellation, for instance Pisces or Cancer.

If there are no insects around at the time for burning you will need to save some from when they are prevalent. Here are a few examples:

Sun in Taurus is best for all hard-shelled insects.
Sun in Gemini is best for codling moths or ants.
Sun in Cancer is best for snails and slugs, mosquitoes and flies.

Maria Thun has added the refinement of using the moon in the constellation as well as the sun for burning the insect, for instance, the sun in Taurus (bull) and the moon in Taurus. The sun is in Taurus about mid-May to mid-June. The resultant ash can be potentised to D6 or D8, or the ash can be mixed with milk, sugar or wood ashes and spread. The insect pepper should be applied regularly throughout the season.

Rodents

Rudolf Steiner suggests burning the *skin* of rodents (mice, rats, rabbits, possums) when Venus is in conjunction with Scorpio. This occurs in a period of three weeks any time from between mid-October and the first week in January. The actual time this occurs each year can be found in any biodynamic planting calendar or astronomical ephemerus. The burnt skin can be ground up and mixed with ash, milk and sugar and sprinkled lightly over the infected areas. The ash can also be potenised to D6 or D8 and sprinkled over the affected area.

Appendix 5

Planets and the preparations

There is always interest at seminars that I run when there is a discussion on the planets and their relationship to the biodynamic preparations. Also of interest is the planetary connection to the days of the week, and with the human being in relation to the organs of the body, which is so much understood and used in anthroposophical medicine. As well, there are connections with metals, the trees, the crystals, the colours, the cereals and the age period of the human being.

Sunday; sun — gold, ash, ruby, white, heart, wheat
21–42 years, Preparation 501, silica[1]

Monday; moon — silver, cherry tree, moonstone, purple, reproductive, rice
Birth–7 years, Preparation 505, oak bark

Tuesday; Mars — iron, oak, diamond, red, gall bladder, oats,
42–49 years, Preparation 504, nettle

Wednesday; Mercury — quicksilver, elm, topaz, yellow, lungs, millet
7–14 years, Preparation 503, chamomile

Thursday; Jupiter — tin, maple, sapphire, orange, liver, rye
49–56 years, Preparation 506, dandelion

Friday; Venus — copper, silver birch, agate, green, kidneys, barley
14–21 years, Preparation 502, yarrow

Saturday; Saturn — lead, conifer and beech, onyx, blue, spleen, corn
56–63 years, Preparation 507, valerian

---

1 The Preparation 501 being connected to the sun is my interpretation as I feel the silica is very connected to the light forces of the sun. Likewise Preparation 500 would be connected to the earthy nature of the earth.

Appendix 6

Twenty-one points on animal health, and some remedies

1 Grow quality feed at all times, using biodynamic methods. Always have adequate reserves of fodder on hand.

2 Address mineral requirements of the soil, such as calcium and phosphate.

3 Practise good pasture management. For example, avoid overgrazing or pugging of paddocks during wet periods.

4 Avoid pasture compaction through overuse of heavy machinery which will destroy soil structure and consequently pasture quality.

5 Encourage a wide range of species of pasture plant throughout the farm (see Appendix 6). Include the deeper-rooting grasses such as cocksfoot, phalarus, prairie grass, as well as legumes such as white and red clover and lucerne. Chicory is also useful.

6 Use Preparation 500 regularly, two to three times a year in spring and autumn, to improve and maintain soil quality and structure.

7 Apply Preparation 501 to pasture — particularly to the hay and silage paddocks — in spring, in the morning, according to the appropriate moon rhythm to enhance fodder quality.

8 Use Preparations 502–507 regularly by means of compost, various liquid manures or cowpat pit so as to bring their influences over the whole farm. These preparations allow the energies of the planets to balance the trace elements and major nutrients, and thus give the soil the ability to grow health-giving plants. The beneficial effect on animal health of the regular and adequate use of these preparations is obvious to all biodynamic farmers.

9 Make quality silage and hay. Perfect your method. Cut your crop at the time of the appropriate moon rhythms.

10 Stock your farm at a sensible and realistic density for your area. Do not overstock.

11 Good shelter from prevailing winds will reduce stress from wind chill, and also enable better grass growth over a longer period.

12 Have good shade trees available to stock, particularly where ultraviolet light levels are high.

13 Have clean water available at all times. Take care not to have wet areas around troughs where diseases and parasites can breed.

14 Avoid other forms of stress on animals at all times. For example, take care when working animals in the yards. Avoid noisy motorbikes and over-enthusiastic dogs.

15 Set stock on drystock units where possible, to avoid the pecking-order syndrome which arises from frequent changes of paddock.

16 Allow longer than the normally accepted times before the weaning of young stock — particularly the dairy calves or lambs you intend to keep for fattening or breeding.

17 Look to the genetic base of your animals. Some diseases are hereditary. Breed for health as well as for weight gain. Check that the sire with a good health record does in fact give you progeny of a good size.

18 Use herbal medicines. Strong drenches of garlic and cider vinegar are a great help with many internal parasites (see below). Use homeopathic remedies where applicable.

19 Make regular additions of herbs to fodder diet, eg rosemary, tansy, wormwood, thyme or sage. See Juliette de Baraicli Levy, *Complete Herbal Handbook for Farm and Stable*, for further information.

20 Make regular additions of cider vinegar to water troughs and onto hay during the winter feeding-out time.

21 Develop the ability to be able to assess the health of your flock or herd with one glance. An early diagnosis of any problem makes for a greater chance of success with a cure.

Herbal drenches and tinctures

Sheep drench cocktail

The following herbal tincture, consisting of cider vinegar, fresh garlic juice, molasses and kelp, can be incorporated in animal drenches. The chemical constituents of the tincture or herbal preparation are extracted into the vinegar, which will dissolve nearly all the relevant ingredients of the herbs and at the same time act as a preservative.

To make a tincture in large quantities, use approximately 0.5–1kg of fresh herbs in a 25-litre bucket of cider vinegar. This is left to brew for at least two weeks in a warm place, and stirred daily. After decanting the bulk of the liquid, pour off the residue into a muslin cloth and wring out all the remaining liquid. The residue makes excellent compost and these tinctures will last indefinitely if stored in a dark place.

Herbs for internal parasites

To cleanse the body of internal parasites, use anthelmintic herbs, eg:

Wormwood – use the flowering tops in moderation due to its bitter taste. The volatile oil it contains is extremely potent.

Tansy – use leaves and flowering tops, also in moderation as large doses can cause abortion during pregnancy.

Pumpkin seed – use ripe seeds as fresh as possible. Crush them up and add to vinegar.

Nasturtium – use leaves and seeds. Nasturtium is richly medicinal as a tonic and cleanser.

Stinging nettle – use leaves and roots. This herb is rich in minerals.

Nutritive and calmative herbs

Tinctures can also be made from nutritive herbs such as plantain, dandelion and chickweed (use the whole plant, roots and foliage), and from calmative herbs such as chamomile (flowering tops) and valerian (root only), which are used to drench animals before they are transported to the abattoir.

Drench to combat lice

Sulphur can be made up to a 12D potency as a means of combating lice in stock. The sulphur is dynamised with lactose, as this makes the sulphur water-soluble. A few drops are put into the sheep drench and also into the cattle water-trough.

The cattle will drink the natural drench from a trough, although it is best to orally drench young cattle so they get a taste for it. Stock should be brought into the yards to fast overnight before drenching. Water with potentised sulphur added should be available at all times. The animals should be drenched in the morning (lambs 10ml twice daily; sheep 20ml twice daily; young cattle 100ml twice daily), left for 3–4 hours, then drenched again in the afternoon before returning to pasture.

Stress in stock

Since the animals are drenched fortnightly from a young age, they become used to the process. They are less stressed by it, are easier to muster and handle, and generally more responsive to humans. In time, all stock can be trained to take the drench from troughs.

Roxanne Gilbert, sheep farmer
Dannevirke
New Zealand

Appendix 7

A herbal ley seed mixture

Note: this mixture was developed by Grasslands, DSIR (now AgResearch) for New Zealand conditions (ie a temperate climate). Consult local agronomists for other species which will grow well in your district.

This mixture contains legumes for nitrogen fixation; many deep-rooted species which tolerate drought, increase soil porosity, and access more minerals; several herbs with high mineral content; and species which give a low risk of sheep facial eczema. Not all species will grow in all districts. Sow in early autumn or early spring.

Recommended sowing rate is 11.5kg (25lb) per acre. The species in the mixture are in approximate balance on a seed-weight basis.

1 *Chicory* — 'Puna': a persistent deep tap-rooted pasture herb which is high-producing, high in minerals and has high-quality summer forage. Excellent animal performance has been recorded with this species. It is suited to free-draining soils.

2 *Yarrow* — a mineral-rich forage herb, persistent, with an extensive rhizome system.

3 *Sheep's burnet* — a fast-establishing perennial herb producing palatable summer forage. Performs well in dry, low-fertility sites and withstands cold winters.

4 *Plantain* — narrow-leaf plantain: deep-rooted summer-growing herb.

5 *Trefoil* — a deep-rooted legume, non-bloating, excellent summer growth, particularly suited to dry, acid, low-fertility soils.

6 *Lucerne* — 'Oranga': deep tap-rooted legume, very drought-tolerant, producing quality summer forage.

7 *Sulla* — 'Aokau': short-lived perennial legume, rapid establishment, very productive during winter. Produces non-bloating forage.

8 *Subterranean clover* — an annual legume, low-growing, with excellent winter growth, able to persist through vigorous reseeding, thus surviving dry summers.

9 *Pink serradella* — 'Koha': a deep-rooted winter annual legume, tolerant of acid soils.

10 *White clover* — 'Pitau': a persistent legume adapted to a wide range of environments. Creeping, prostrate habit with a network of spreading stolons.

11 *Red clover* — 'Pawera' and 'Hamua': a tap-rooted perennial legume. Produces high-quality summer forage and is drought-tolerant. Early and late flowering types combined.

12 *Prairie grass* — 'Matua': a perennial grass with a good winter growth. Best suited to higher-fertility soils that are free-draining. Grows well during winter and dry summers.

13 *Yorkshire Fog* — 'Massey Basin': a perennial grass, very palatable. Grows well on low-fertility and acid soils.

14 *Browntop* — 'Muster': pasture browntop suitable for low-fertility and acid soils. A perennial grass with a dense rhizomatous growth habit.

15 *Hybrid ryegrass* — 'Greenstone': a persistent tetraploid hybrid ryegrass, very palatable. No endophyte, giving excellent winter/spring growth. Tillers strongly.

16 *Cocksfoot* — 'Wana': a perennial ryegrass with a deep root-system, well adapted to dry, low-fertility soils. Active over the summer.

17 *Phalarus* — 'Maru': perennial grass with active cool-season growth. Tolerant of dry, harsh environments and of insect pests, including grassgrub.

18 *Timothy* — 'Kahu': high forage-quality grass, especially good on moist sites.

Appendix 8

Conversion from metric to imperial equivalents

Square measure
> 1 hectare = 2.471 acres

Cubic measure
> 1 cubic metre = 1.308 cu. yards

Capacity measure
> 1 millilitre = 0.002 pint (British)
> 1 litre = 1.76 pints
> 10 litres = 2.20 gallons

Weight
> 1 kilogram = 2.205 pounds
> 1 tonne (1000 kg) = 0.984 (long) ton

Source: *The Concise Oxford Dictionary*, 8th edn, 1990.

Appendix 9
Biodynamic associations — contact details

Biodynamic associations throughout the world provide some or all of the following services for their members:

- ⊚ information and advice

- ⊚ sale of preparations

- ⊚ directories of suppliers for various resources

- ⊚ farm inspection and certification to Demeter standards

- ⊚ educational seminars, discussion groups, courses in biodynamic methods.

New Zealand   The BioDynamic Farming and Gardening Association
            in New Zealand (Inc.)
            PO Box 39045, Wellington Mail Centre, New Zealand.
            Ph +64 4 589 5366, fax +64 4 589 5365
            Email biodynamics@clear.net.nz

Australia   Biodynamic AgriCulture Australia
            PO Box 54, Bellingen, NSW 2454, Australia.
            Ph +61 2 6655 0566, fax +61 2 6655 0565
            Email bdoffice@biodynamics.net.au

USA   Biodynamic Farming and Gardening Association (Inc.)
            Building 1002B, Thoreau Centre, The Presidio,
            PO Box 29135, San Francisco, CA 94129 0135, USA.
            Ph +1 415 561 7797
            Email biodynamic@aol.com

Canada   Bio-Dynamic Agricultural Society of British Columbia
            Skimikin Road, CDN-Chase, BC VOE 1MO, Canada.
            Ph +1 604 679 8052, fax +1 604 679 2932

Hawaii   Biodynamics Hawaii
            2514 Alaula Way, Honolulu, HI 96822, Hawaii, USA.
            Ph +1 808 988 4555
            Email pdwyer@compuserve.com

United Kingdom   Biodynamic Agricultural Association
Painswick Inn, Gloucester Street, Stroud, Gloucestershire GL5 1QG, UK.
Ph +44 145 375 9501
Email bdaa@biodynamic.freeserve.co.uk

India   Bio Dynamic Association of India
No 78, 1st Floor, 11th Cross, Indiranagar 1st Stage, Bangalore,
  Karnataka, India.
Ph +91 80 528 5883
Email bdai@vsnl.net or skk21@sancharnet.in

Germany   Forschungsring für biol.-dyn.
Wirtschaftsweise, Brandschneise 2, D-64295 Darmstadt, Germany.
Ph +49 6155 846 981 or 846 999, fax +49 6155 846 911
Email c.hauenschild@demeter.de

Ireland   Bio-Dynamic Agricultural Association in Ireland
Ballinroan House, IRL-Kiltegan, Co. Wicklow, Ireland.
Fax + 353 508 81006

South Africa   Bio-Dynamic Agricultural Association of Southern Africa
PO Box 115, Paulshof, South Africa 2056.
Ph + 27 11 803 1688
Email bdoca@telkomsa.net

There are also associations in Quebec and Ontario in Canada, and in Austria, Brazil, Denmark, Finland, France, Israel, Italy, Croatia, Luxembourg, Netherlands, Norway, Sweden, Switzerland, Slovenia and Spain.

Bibliography

Baraicli Levy, Juliette de, 1976. *Complete Herbal Handbook for Farm and Stable*, Rodale Press, Emmaus, PA.

BioDynamic Farming & Gardening Association in New Zealand, published annually. *BioDynamic Farming and Gardening Calendar*, Napier.

Bockemuhl, Jochen, 1981. *In Partnership with Nature*, Bio-Dynamic Literature, Wyoming, RI.

Carter, Neil, 1989. 'Some new research aspects of biodynamics', in *Biodynamics — New Directions for Farming and Gardening in New Zealand*, Random Century NZ, Auckland.

Grohmann, G, 1974. *The Plant*, 2 vols, Rudolf Steiner Press, London.

Koenig, K, 1982. *Earth and Man*, Biodynamic Literature, Wyoming.

Koepf, Herbert H, 1987. *The Biodynamic Farm: Agriculture in Service of the Earth and Humanity*, Anthroposophic Press, Bells Pond, NY.

Kolisko, Eugen & Lilli, 1978. *Agriculture of Tomorrow*, Kolisko Archive Publications, Bournemouth.

Leivegoed, BCJ, 1951. *The Workings of the Planets and Life Processes in Man and Earth*, Experimental Circle of Anthroposophical Farmers & Gardeners, Clent.

Levick, Mark, 1991. 'Comparisons of organic and conventional orchard floor management', Honours thesis, Massey University, Palmerston North.

MacGregor, AN, 1996, pers. communication.

Mortimer, John & Bunny, 1984. *Trees for the New Zealand Countryside*, Silverfish, Auckland.

Pearce, Norrie, 1989. *A Biodynamic Farmer's Handbook*, AN Pearce, PO Box 26295, Epsom, Auckland.

Pfeiffer, Ehrenfried, 1983. *Soil Fertility, Renewal and Preservation*, Lanthorn Press, East Grinstead.

Pfeiffer, Ehrenfried, 1960. 'Chromatography applied to quality testing', Biodynamic Farming & Gardening Association, Stroudsberg, PA.

Reganold, John P, AS Palmer, JC Lockhart & AN Macgregor, 1993. 'Soil quality and financial performance of biodynamic and conventional farms in New Zealand', *Science* 260, 16 April.

Schwenk, Theodor, 1965. *Sensitive Chaos: The Creation of Flowing Forms in Water and Air*, Rudolf Steiner Press, London.

Steiner, Rudolf, 1970. *Man as Symphony of the Creative World*, Rudolf Steiner Press, London.

Steiner, Rudolf, 1993. *Agriculture*, trans. CE Creeger & M Gardner, Bio-Dynamic Farming & Gardening Association, Kimberton, PA.

Thun, Maria, 1979. *Working on the Land and the Constellations*, Lanthorn Press, East Grinstead.

Thun, Maria, 1999. *Gardening for Life the Biodynamic Way*, Hawthorne Press, Stroud, Gloucestershire.

Van Stensil, 1994, pers. communication.

Wachsmuth, Guenther, 1932. *The Etheric Formative Forces*, Anthroposophical Publishing, London.

Willis, Harold, 1985. *The Coming Revolution in Agriculture*, A.R. Editions, Wisconsin.

Index